THE STORY
OF SEX

THE STORY OF SEX

OF SEX

FROM APES TO ROBOTS

FRENCH WORDS: **PHILIPPE BRENOT**
IMAGES: **LAETITIA CORYN**
ENGLISH WORDS: **WILL MCMORRAN**
COLOURS: **ISABELLE LEBEAU**

PENGUIN BOOKS

We would especially like to thank Laurent
Muller, Catherine Meyer and Laurent
Beccaria for agreeing to our utopian dream
of publishing this impertinent history
of sexuality.

PENGUIN BOOKS

UK | USA | Canada | Ireland | Australia
India | New Zealand | South Africa

Penguin Books is part of the Penguin Random
House group of companies whose addresses can
be found at global.penguinrandomhouse.com.

Penguin
Random House
UK

First published in France by les arènes BD 2016
This translation first published in Particular Books 2016
Published in Penguin Books 2019
001

Text copyright © Philippe Brenot and Laetitia Coryn,
2016.
The moral right of the authors has been asserted

English translation © Will McMorran, 2016

Printed and bound in Italy by L.E.G.O. S.p.A.

A CIP catalogue record for this book is available
from the British Library

ISBN: 978-0-141-98527-5

MIX
Paper from
responsible sources
FSC® C018179

Penguin Random House is committed to a
sustainable future for our business, our readers
and our planet. This book is made from Forest
Stewardship Council® certified paper.

www.greenpenguin.co.uk

CONTENTS

CLOSELY GUARDED SECRETS VII

1   ORIGINS 1

2   BABYLON: FREE LOVE 19

3   EGALITARIAN EGYPT 31

4   GREECE: PANTHEON OF LOVE....................................45

5   ROME: GREATNESS AND DECADENCE 65

6   THE MIDDLE AGES: HEAVEN AND HELL 79

7   THE RENAISSANCE: THE ARTIST AND HIS MODEL.........97

8   THE M WORD 111

9   THE ENLIGHTENMENT: REPRESSION AND LIBERTINAGE 121

10 THE 19TH CENTURY: CLENCHED BUTTOCKS AND PROSTITUTION ...139

11 THE 20TH CENTURY: SEXUAL LIBERATION 157

12 THE 21ST CENTURY: FUTURESEX 175

    MEMO 185

CLOSELY GUARDED SECRETS

The Story of Sex lifts the lid on closely guarded secrets and old wives' tales to reveal what has long been hidden from us: the story of sex and love.

How did our sexual organs change when we evolved from animal to human? When did the first couple show up? Where does our sense of modesty come from? Or eroticism? Or love, that most momentous of human concerns? What about our earliest customs? Is prostitution really the "oldest profession in the world"? Was homosexuality really accepted in antiquity? What were the earliest rituals for warding off impotence? Which ancient civilization championed equality between men and women? How did Ramesses contribute to the fertility of Egypt? And why was masturbation prohibited? No history textbook will ever tell you all this because it delves too far into the sexual realm – still a taboo in our society, however free its customs may be.

Do scholarly books tell us about Cleopatra's "fellatory" compulsion with her guards? About Priapus's ways with the women of Lampsacus? About the phallic festivals of antiquity – of Dionysia and Bacchanalia? About chastity belts or the *droit du seigneur*? No respectable historian would venture down the slippery slope of everyday exploits of sex and intimacy. Though these stories are genuine they are generally consigned to the margins by official history. However, this little chronicle of sexual habits can offer us a clearer understanding of the extraordinary evolution in customs which has led us from an existence ordered by family and society, and reinforced by religion, to the freedoms we know today in the West.

History books gloss over the idiosyncrasies of famous figures, but their sex lives help us to understand them better. Does anyone today talk about Casanova, the Marquis de Sade, the Chevalier d'Éon, or the libertines of the Directory during the French Revolution? Have you heard about the hypersexuality of Henry IV or Louis XV? Or Queen Victoria's sex life? Or Prince Albert's genital piercing? As well-known as the homosexuality of Michelangelo, Leonardo da Vinci or Montaigne may be, it still has no place in their "official" biographies. *The Story of Sex* sets the record straight.

There are still many misconceptions that circulate in private, shying away from awkward questions: the difference between homosexuality and pederasty, between male need and female desire, between vaginal and clitoral women… Still more shadowy realms where *The Story of Sex* can shine a light.

At the start of this third millennium, sexuality seems to be all around us – within easy reach, shown on our screens, talked about in the media – but, paradoxically, it's rarely explained and almost never taught. In our schools there is no real sex education. At the very most, some information about contraception and STDs. But nothing that helps to understand the nature of intimate relationships, or the difficulties of developing these, or the vital link between respect and equality between partners, or questions about sexual orientation… And in this educational void, the internet and porn offer themselves as models.

The Story of Sex reveals this essential aspect of human intimacy.

PHILIPPE BRENOT
LAETITIA CORYN

CHAPTER 1

ORIGINS

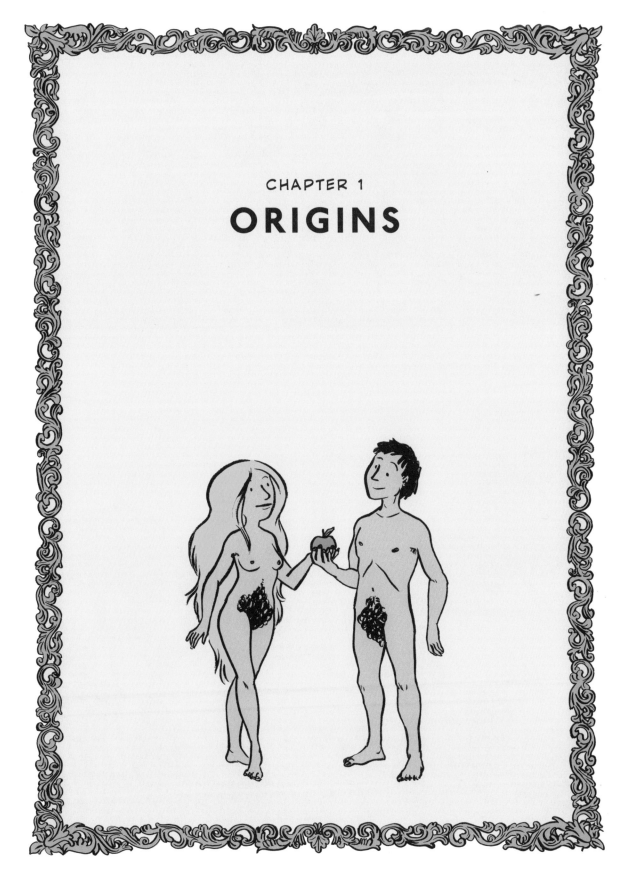

The history of OUR sexuality began a very long time ago in the forests of East Africa, that region that gave birth to US — to humans — and where our cousins the chimpanzees still live today.

Two million years ago, a small group of hominoids venture from the tropical forest of their forebears to begin the great human adventure. They settle down near sources of water, notably in Chad and in the Great Rift Valley, which slices through East Africa from north to south from the Ethiopia to the Zimbabwe of today.

These hominoids already resemble us in many ways. Their stature is starting to straighten and — a sign of modernity — they are walking on two feet.

Though smaller than us, they still have attributes that hark back to their origins: they are still hairy except for their faces, where features now appear that we would regard as "human" today.

BEFORE

AND ALL THAT IN JUST A FEW MILLION YEARS.

AFTER

TURNS OUT I'M FEMALE?

Four great innovations will mark the transition to human sexuality:

1/THE LOSS OF THE OESTRUS*
Now they can make love all year round!

BEFORE

AFTER

* The "red buttocks" of the female chimpanzee mark the period they are on heat, known as the "oestrus".

2/THE LOSS OF THE PENIS BONE*
Now man can stand erect without any support: no need for a bone! His penis is longer, thicker, stronger!

♪ AAAAA... ♫

*All primates have a small bone to maintain an erection.

3/THE INVENTION OF THAT LOVING FEELING, which will become humanity's great preoccupation!

CAN YOU FEEEL

♫ THE LOVE TONIIIGHT ♫

*A slight but deliberate anachronism to add to the romantic mood. This was before Elton John was born.

4/But on the down side, MALE DOMINATION and the subjection of females — which will profoundly affect humanity right up to our own day*.

OK! YOU CAN HAVE THE THIGH!

OFF TO A GOOD START!

* Among primates, the males don't dominate the females — or even interact with them much. They are two separate but cohabiting worlds.

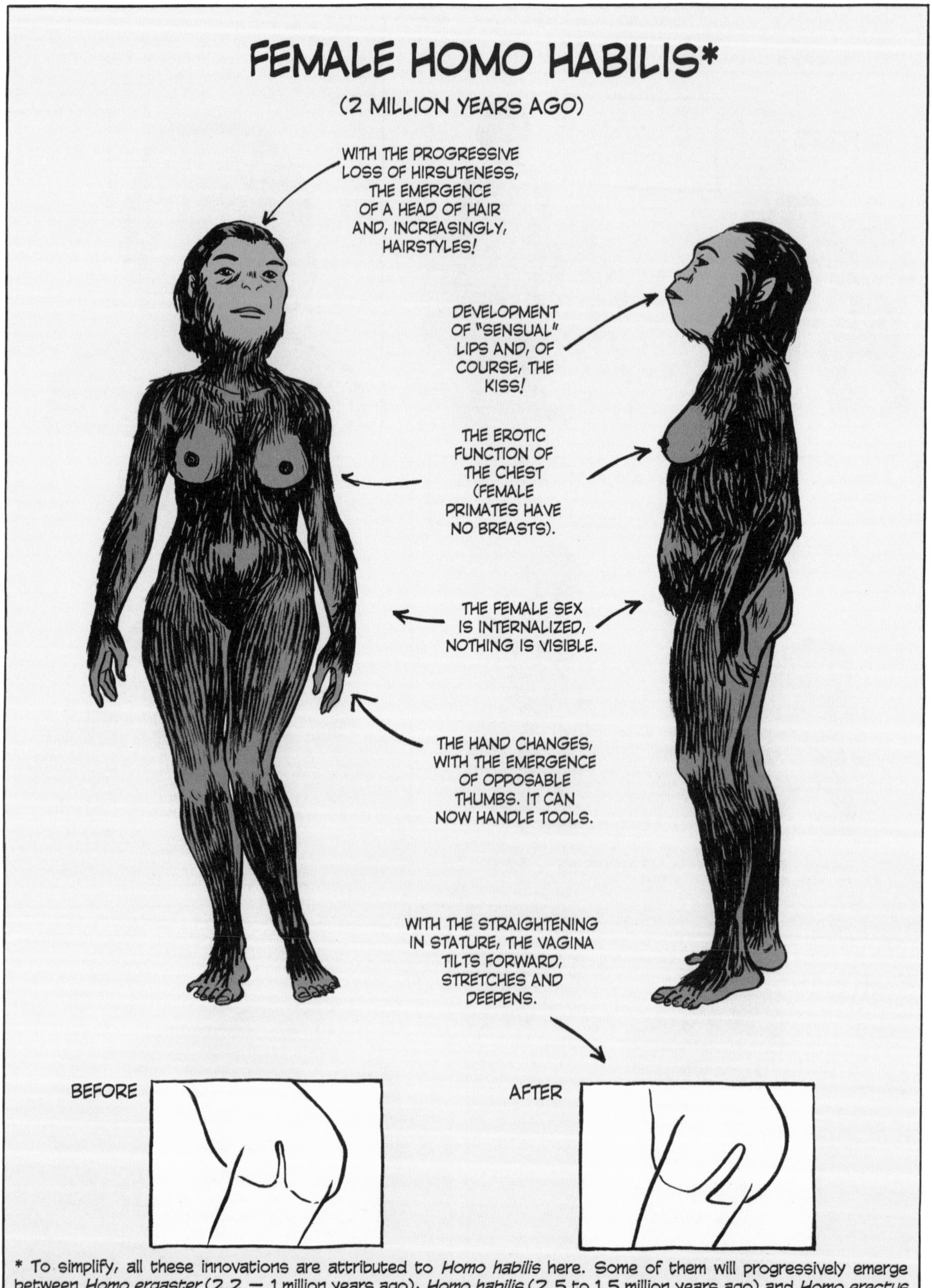

FEMALE HOMO HABILIS*

(2 MILLION YEARS AGO)

WITH THE PROGRESSIVE LOSS OF HIRSUTENESS, THE EMERGENCE OF A HEAD OF HAIR AND, INCREASINGLY, HAIRSTYLES!

DEVELOPMENT OF "SENSUAL" LIPS AND, OF COURSE, THE KISS!

THE EROTIC FUNCTION OF THE CHEST (FEMALE PRIMATES HAVE NO BREASTS).

THE FEMALE SEX IS INTERNALIZED, NOTHING IS VISIBLE.

THE HAND CHANGES, WITH THE EMERGENCE OF OPPOSABLE THUMBS. IT CAN NOW HANDLE TOOLS.

WITH THE STRAIGHTENING IN STATURE, THE VAGINA TILTS FORWARD, STRETCHES AND DEEPENS.

BEFORE

AFTER

* To simplify, all these innovations are attributed to *Homo habilis* here. Some of them will progressively emerge between *Homo ergaster* (2.2 — 1 million years ago), *Homo habilis* (2.5 to 1.5 million years ago) and *Homo erectus* (1.8 million to 200 000 years ago). *Homo habilis* is the first true man.

MALE HOMO HABILIS
(2 MILLION YEARS AGO)

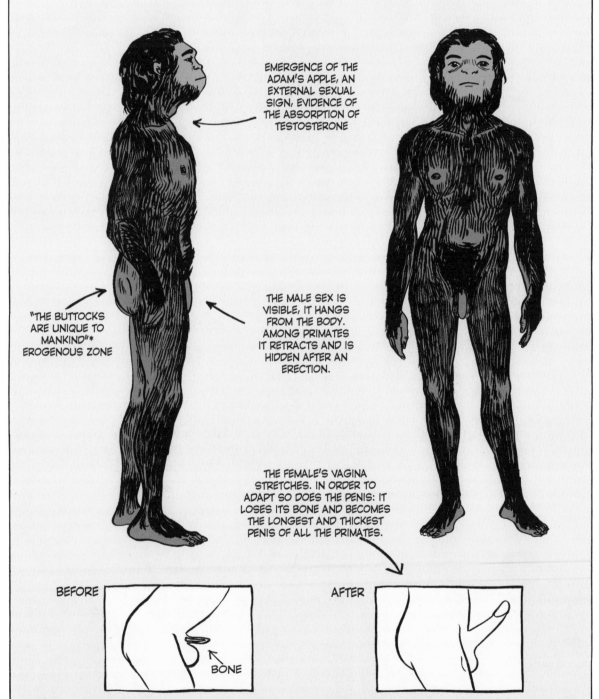

EMERGENCE OF THE ADAM'S APPLE, AN EXTERNAL SEXUAL SIGN, EVIDENCE OF THE ABSORPTION OF TESTOSTERONE

"THE BUTTOCKS ARE UNIQUE TO MANKIND"* EROGENOUS ZONE

THE MALE SEX IS VISIBLE, IT HANGS FROM THE BODY. AMONG PRIMATES IT RETRACTS AND IS HIDDEN AFTER AN ERECTION.

THE FEMALE'S VAGINA STRETCHES. IN ORDER TO ADAPT SO DOES THE PENIS: IT LOSES ITS BONE AND BECOMES THE LONGEST AND THICKEST PENIS OF ALL THE PRIMATES.

BEFORE

BONE

AFTER

*Indeed, monkeys have no bottoms. Walking upright, which strengthens the buttock muscles, has endowed man with a "rounded" behind which is today one of the main attractors for men as well as women.

We are going to follow a small group of hominoids. This will allow us to highlight the characteristics of these early humans, their way of life, their intimacy and their sexuality.

WUU
40 YEARS OLD
ELDERLY FEMALE

SOHO
25 YEARS OLD
THIRD FEMALE

NOAH
20 YEARS OLD
IN LOVE WITH SAW

HIGO
40 YEARS OLD
ALPHA MALE

YAWA
30 YEARS OLD
ALPHA FEMALE

SAW
15 YEARS OLD
ALREADY A MOTHER
IN LOVE WITH NOAH

ZINN
30 YEARS OLD
BETA MALE

The group is busy searching for fruit and roots, rare in the savannah. Zinn and Noah hunt small mammals that they kill for food.

In the hostile savannah, there are many predators: hyenas, big cats, or crocodiles near water-sources.

They remain vigilant as other groups of hominoids, whose rivalry they fear, are close by.

The new humans progressively adapt to running. They lose their hairiness, which had been suited to the forest, and this gives way to sweat glands that allow them to regulate exertion through perspiration. Man is a "naked ape", to use Desmond Morris's term.

Hindered in his running by this "thing" hanging between his legs, Noah invents an athletic support made from vines. It's the first G-string — THE INVENTION OF CLOTHING.

THREE GREAT RULES ARE RESPECTED IN THIS EGALITARIAN PROTOSOCIETY.

First great rule: OPPORTUNISM, such as when a carcass is discovered...

Second great rule: SHARING.

There is already mutual assistance among the males in order to look after the little ones.

Third great rule: DOMINANCE: Higo, the alpha male, is first in line for food as he's the strongest. It's brute force which determines the order in which they eat ...

... and have sex!

7

Male domination stems from the dominance demanded by the competition around food. The females are grouped around Higo. He is their protector but also their master. Polygyny (one male and multiple females) prevailed in the early days of humanity.

The females are in a way rendered "immobile" by their care of the children. The little ones stay close to them until they are 5 or 6 years old.

C'MON PUBERTY!

FOOD!

FOOD!

FOOD!

FOOD!

The children belong to the group. No one yet has any sense of who the fathers are!

HOW ABOUT YOU LOOKING AFTER YOUR KIDS FOR A BIT?

MY WHAT?

But there are already two coexisting worlds: that of the women around the children, and that of the men — more mobile, hunters...

WHERE'S HE GOING?

SOMEWHERE I'LL NEVER GO...

And already an argument between males over a female...

MINE!

MINE!

MINE!

OK.

OK.

With Saw and Noah, love will try to lay down its own law.

Throughout the whole human adventure, love will try to intervene in the affairs of the group, the clan, the family... but very often the group's interests will be stronger. Fortunately, strength of feeling thrives on adversity and lovers will not have the wool pulled over their eyes.

This morning, Zinn, the 30-year-old male, is very aroused... He really wants to mate with Saw.

BIFF!

Noah, jealous, intervenes.

And Zinn beats his retreat. He's lost.

9

Noah and Saw nonetheless both respect the rule of dominance. If Higo decides to mate with Saw, he will do as he pleases.

As for Zinn, he tries to approach Wuu, the oldest female of the group...

... who rebuffs him violently.

So it's to Soho he now turns...

... and he forces her to mate with him. This is **THE FIRST RAPE.**

I MOURN FOR THE TIME OF MY GREAT AUNT CHIMPANZEE, WHO CHOSE HER MALES FOR HERSELF!

Saw approaches Noah again.

They look at each other, touch each other, cuddle each other... This is the invention of TENDER LOVE.

They wander off together...

PURR
PURR
PURR

... and for the first time, they make love.

One great novelty about human sex: unlike the primates who mate in full view of everyone, the lovers hide themselves away to make love. They do it far from prying eyes.
This is THE INVENTION OF MODESTY

We are witnessing THE DISCOVERY OF LOVE, that very powerful feeling that binds humans together.

Love, a characteristic of the human race.

THE BIBLE AND THE BEGINNING

Each culture codifies the history of our origins in a founding story, one which organizes that society by laying down the essential rules of life for the generations to come. In the case of the three great monotheistic religions (Judaism, Christianity, Islam), the founding story is based on a genesis, the gist of which we shall summarize very loosely here.

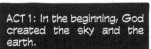

ACT 1: In the beginning, God created the sky and the earth.

To drive out the darkness, he created light...

THAT'S BETTER!

Next he created the sea and the land, where trees and flowers spread...

He created the animals that inhabit the earth and the birds that fly through the air...

And he put the moon, the sun and the stars in the sky... and all that in five days!

DIDN'T HANG ABOUT, DID I?

ACT 2: On the sixth day, he said to himself, "Let us make man in our own image." He created Adam, the first man, and made him flesh.

HAPPY?

OH YES, DAD!

CLAY
CLAY

He put the finishing touches to man's sex and gave him one prohibition:

YOU SHALL NOT EAT THE FRUIT FROM THE TREE OF KNOWLEDGE.

Then he thought to himself: "It is not good for man to be alone." He put Adam to sleep, took one of his ribs, and from this rib created Eve, the first woman.

God thus created the first couple, a man and a woman. They were both naked but were not ashamed as they were not conscious of this.

12

ACT 3: It is at this point that a young seducer — the serpent — approached the woman, and tried to tempt her...

TASTE MY LOVELY APPLE!

YOUR EYES WILL BE OPENED. YOU WILL BE A PRINCESS AND ADAM WILL BE YOUR GOD.

Curious, Eve took a bite from the apple and offered it to Adam, who shared in the forbidden fruit.

TASTE IT — IT'S YUMMY!

OK!

At that moment, they realized they were naked!

Offended, God banished them from paradise, condemning them to wander and suffer.

WHAT ARE WE TO MAKE OF THIS STORY?
A symbolic reading tells us that it is about the transition from nature to culture, the emergence of consciousness, of prohibitions and of guilt. The awareness of nudity seems to mark the beginning of humanity. It is the invention of modesty, a human characteristic.

A more iconoclastic reading tells us that the serpent is a subversive seducer (psychoanalysis claims the serpent is a phallus).

He was quick to bewitch Eve, who took a bite from the forbidden fruit — the first breach of contract, the first act of adultery. As original sin is the knowledge of sex, all sexual prohibitions stem from this moment.

It is also said that Eve gave birth to Cain but it is later stated that Cain was not Adam's son...

Which suggests that he could only be the child of the serpent, and thus of adultery!

YOU KNOW, THERE ARE TIMES WHEN I WONDER...

WELL, I CAN'T SEE WHY...

The next part of the story is never really repeated. Here, exclusively, is the gist of it...

Eve first had two sons. Cain was a farmer and Abel a shepherd.

Out of jealousy, Cain killed Abel.

OUCH!

God condemned him to wander the earth.

Cain took a wife. This could only have been his own mother, as Adam and Eve were the only other humans.!

YOU'VE GOT A NERVE.

AS IF I HAD ANY CHOICE...

Within the Jewish tradition, it is said that Adam and Eve had 33 sons and 23 daughters. Humanity is thus born from their couplings.

We can only conclude from this evidence: in the beginning was incest...

13

We are now on the western edge of Europe, in the valley of Vézère in the south-west of France, where Cro-Magnon man has reigned since the Neanderthals died out. We are now 20 000 years BC, at the time of the last ice age, and the climate is very harsh...

Humans have evolved — they move around in organized groups, use spoken language (and have been for over 100 000 years!)...

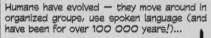

... live in shelters at the foot of limestone cliffs...

...bury their dead...

Men and women take part in communal life, hunt, gather, carve tools... They wear jewels, finery, style their hair. There is already a sense of fashion.

The men are very preoccupied by a great mystery...

They explore caves, damp holes, narrow passages, womb-metaphors...

The men depict that mysterious part of a woman's body where children come from.

The mystery of childbirth inhabits the newly formed subconscious of our ice-age ancestors.

They represent women as mothers, symbols of fertility, and depict female genitals, rarely phalluses.

They even create rituals...

A sorcerer armed with a phallus dances around female figurines.

If there was in the beginning a natural male dominance rooted in our primate past, and notably in relation to food, a form of masculine domination now takes hold which (sadly) characterizes the whole of humanity. This domination of females by males will progressively take hold from 1 million to 100000 years ago, though we can't be more precise than that.

This stems in great part from men's realization of their role in conception.

SHOW SOME RESPECT! WITHOUT ME, THERE WOULDN'T BE ANY CHILDREN!

YEAH, WELL — NOT WITHOUT THIS EITHER!

The power of the eldest establishes itself over the youngest and over their female progenitors — women. Sex (male) and age are the two sources of power.

SO STAY OUT OF IT ALL RIGHT, MY LITTLE GROUCHES?

FOR DARWIN

THE "PRIMITIVE HORDE" ORGANIZES ITSELF AROUND A VERY POWERFUL MALE; HE PROVIDES FOR AND PROTECTS SEVERAL FEMALES, BUT FORBIDS THEM FROM ANY CONTACT WITH THE OTHER MALES.

GRRRR...

MINE!

The old law of exogamy, which has existed since the time of the primates, becomes an instrument of power in the hands of men: every girl is now her father's property, and thus becomes a form of currency (isn't this the very start of property?).

SHE'S PRETTY, MY DAUGHTER!

SHE'S PRETTY!

STOP IT, DAD, THE NEIGHBOURS WILL SEE US!

THAT'S THE IDEA.

In return, the father gives up on consuming the goods himself, establishing the value of virginity and the prohibition on incest, but also the invention of marriage.

THERE'S MY GIRL — ALL SHINY AND NEW!

EVEN I HAVEN'T LAID A FINGER ON HER!

JUST AS WELL...

Though incest still happens...

FOR FREUD

STOP! TABOO!

A Freudian slip-up (not that he knew it!): the incest taboo, that fundamental law from the dawn of humanity, has, however, existed for a long time. **Among our primate cousins,** and among our earliest ancestors, the avoidance of incest is already in force and is far more respected than it would be by humanity.

Young females change groups at puberty (exogamy), and this way they don't encounter either their father or their brothers.

WHERE'S SHE GOING, YOUR DAUGHTER?

TO THE NEIGHBOURS, TO FIND HERSELF A BOYFRIEND.

And the mothers are very quick to distance themselves from their offspring, before the bond between them becomes too intimate.

GO ON! SCRAM, YOU LITTLE WEIRDO!

BUT, MUM...

Humanity now establishes this prohibition as a fundamental, organizing law for all societies.

FOR LEVI-STRAUSS

THE INCEST PROHIBITION

The avoidance practised by animals is now communicated linguistically through stories — such as the myth of Oedipus.

HEY, OEDIPUS! GO FUCK YOUR MOTHER!

But like every other law, this one is made to be transgressed.

MY CHILD, NO ONE MARRIES THEIR PARENTS...

NO, YOU LITTLE FREAK...

BUT HE'S SO CUTE...

The human incest taboo is thus far less respected than the avoidance practised by animals!

ZINN!

STOP BOTHERING YOUR SISTER!

We are now a little further south, 15 000 years ago, in the Magdeleine cave in today's Tarn region in France.

These men are fascinated by the female sex. They have depicted it a thousand times.

The figures of these women, who attract them and who make babies, fill them with admiration...

... and the rock serves as a canvas for the attraction they feel for their female companions. There is no doubt that the notion of beauty exists from this point on. The first visual depiction of beauty was certainly feminine.

We are in Babylon, Mesopotamia, part of today's Iraq — one of the oldest cities of human civilization, 1700 years BC.

Writing already has a thousand-year history, and scribes record the life of this mythical city in detail.

IF YOU'RE NAUGHTY, THAT MAN WILL WRITE IT DOWN.

AND EVERYONE WILL STILL BE READING ABOUT IT IN 3000 YEARS!

Cuneiform script (Sumerian, then Akkadian) is humanity's first great system of writing.

NOT A GOOD NEWS DAY.

Humans have now settled, and marriage is important in this very patriarchal society where family plays a huge role.

But already the relationship of dependence between men and women is clearly codified as it will be for millennia.

MARRIAGE

The family is based on a marriage between spouses often chosen as young children by their respective families. Higo, Saw's father and a rich merchant from Uruk, has pledged his daughter to Noah, the son of his friend, Enoki.

This marriage will allow them to join forces and trade together between Babylon and Uruk.

On her wedding day, the young bride — Saw is 13 years old — leaves her family to live with Noah's.

WELCOME TO BABYLON, BABY!

She is his one and only wife — for as long as she is fertile. An infertile wife can be repudiated...

YOU'RE THE ONLY ONE FOR ME!

YEAH, BUT AT WHAT PRICE!

Unless she finds a replacement!

SAY, YOU DON'T WANT TO STAND IN FOR ME WITH NOAH, DO YOU?

I'M NOT INFERTILE — I'VE JUST HAD ENOUGH.

As for Noah, he's a man, and in Babylon men are as free as love!

HAVE A GREAT TIME!

OH, YEAH — YOU CAN COUNT ON IT!

In Babylon, where free love is held up as a mark of civilization, Noah has every right to do as he pleases. His wife is his property. He has a few concubines and happily sleeps with the women he fancies.

OH! EXCUSE ME, LADIES — I'LL JUST BE A FEW MINUTES...

Married women wear a veil, unlike the prostitutes who recognize each other from their bare heads — for they are not allowed to look like respectable women.

Having had his fun with a prostitute, Noah now heads with two courtesans to a tavern where anything goes. Wherever you look there are lovers embracing, and the beer flows just as freely.

In a corner of the tavern, Noah sodomizes a prostitute as she calmly sips beer from a straw.*

*An authentic scene described by a scribe!

The scribes in this period were true reporters!

Homosexuality is marginal in Babylon but it is accepted. A homosexual is seen as a man who's effeminate and passive. He doesn't face any condemnation.

For fellatio, the prostitutes coat their clients' penises with honey to improve the taste!

I'M MAKING MYSELF A SNACK IF THAT'S OKAY!

AS LONG AS YOU DON'T TAKE A BITE...

As a good wife, Saw submits to her husband and devotes herself to her children. She stays at home inside the gynaeceum

But, jealous because she truly loves him, Saw tries to seduce another man to provoke her young husband.

Noah notices and gives her an earful.

In this society, where love is free for men (only incest and adultery are prohibited), women are not so lucky, and have very little freedom.

THE SPRING FESTIVAL

It is early March, a little further south in Eridu, at the temple of Ishtar, where everyone is seeing in the new year.

Everyone is celebrating the return of spring, the rebirth of nature.

Prostitutes, recognizable by their long curls, crowd around the temple to entice passers-by. Men have every right to do as they please.

At this time (the new year) there are daily ceremonies.

In the middle of the temple stands the statue of Ishtar, goddess of physical love and of war. She has been dressed in all her finery for the occasion.

During the ceremony, several sheep are sacrificed...

There is a parade of singers and dancers, mimes, cross-dressers, and androgynes to entertain Ishtar, "the Lady of Heaven".

A priestess recites verses from a tablet...

"O Ishtar, make it so that a man's love for a woman is fulfilled... And a woman's love for a man..."

"And a man's love for a man..."

In a crypt in this sanctuary, a man struggles to get hard and, next to him, a priestess encourages him, flatters him, helps him as she performs great cabalistic gestures and recites incantatory verses:

MAY THE WIND BLOW, MAY THE RIVER SWELL...

GN!

It's the FIRST TREATMENT FOR IMPOTENCE.

MAY YOUR PENIS BE AS TAUT AS AN ARROW-STRING, AS STIFF AS A BILLY GOAT'S, AS HARD AS A BULL'S...

COPULATE, COPULATE... DON'T BE SCARED, FOLLOW ISHTAR'S COMMANDMENTS...

KEEP IT UP, KEEP IT UP! BE AS HORNY AS A STAG! AS ERECT AS A WILD BULL!

MAKE LOVE TO ME SIX TIMES LIKE YOU WOULD A NANNY GOAT...

MAKE LOVE TO ME LIKE YOU WOULD A DOE...

MAKE LOVE TO ME TWELVE TIMES LIKE YOU WOULD A PARTRIDGE!

In the great hall, at Ishtar's feet, a bed is prepared. King Hammurabi steps forward before the crowd gathered there.

A voice is raised: in "Hammurabi" there is "amour" (Lacan, II, 8).

A tall and beautiful priestess joins him.

The enraptured crowd pay homage to the sovereign who has just roused nature from her slumbers: it is the festival of the new year, which recalls Ishtar's descent into the underworld.

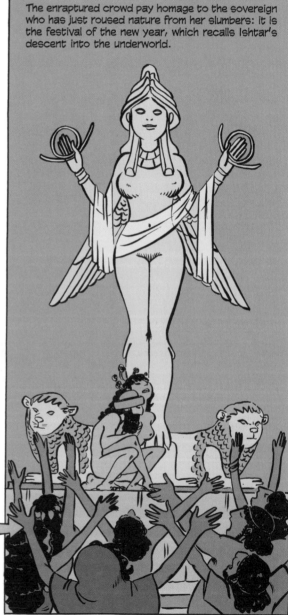

According to an immutable rite, they embrace and make love...

... while Ishtar's priestesses chant their incantations: "Stiff as a billy goat... Harder than a bull..."

28

Ishtar is the prototype for the goddess of love. Aphrodite in Greece and Venus in Rome will be her successors.

Ishtar has very many handsome lovers who can't resist her charms. She has all the men she desires...

Except one: Gilgamesh, King of Uruk, whose exploits are lauded everywhere.

OOH! WHAT A HUNK!

But when she begs him to be her lover, Gilgamesh spurns her with contempt.

FIE ON THEE, FOUL SLUT!

It has to be said that Ishtar had changed one of her suitors into a frog after he touched her sex...

YOU TEASE...

Furious at being rejected, Ishtar begs Anu, God of the sky, to create an invincible animal — the celestial bull, which she sends to Uruk.

GRRR...

Gilgamesh grabs it by the horns and cuts these of with a knife, while his friend Enkidu grabs it by the tail and rips off its penis!

OLÉ!

The two friends wash their hands in the Euphrates and are hailed by the people.

PAF! PAF!

Ishtar, the Lady of the Sky, wanted to be mistress of the underworld as well. She made her descent there — the realm of her sister and sworn enemy, Ereshkigal.

She passed through seven gates, losing an item of clothing after each one.

She thus found herself naked before Ereshkigal who, along with the seven judges of the underworld, condemned her to death.

The death of Ishtar, goddess of fertility and love, caused a cataclysm on earth, bringing life and reproduction to a halt.

This so terrified the gods that they brought her back to life.

COME BACK, ISHTAR!

IT WAS JUST A JOKE!

Enki, god of subterranean waters.

This is why Ishtar's return is celebrated each year in the spring by the marriage/coupling of the god Enki and the goddess Ishtar and, by proxy, the king and a priestess.

CHAPTER 3

EGALITARIAN EGYPT

Ancient Egypt, like Sumer and Babylon, emerges in the third millennium BC, beside the fertile banks of the Nile. It will reach its zenith with the New Kingdom (1500 BC).

It will go on to be colonized first by Alexander the Great's Greece (300 BC) and then by the Roman Empire (30 BC).

The mother of Western civilization, Egypt seems like a society ahead of its time, championing equality between men and women...

I APPRECIATE THAT, DEAR.

AKHENATON

NEFERTITI

... with knowledge of contraception and birth control...

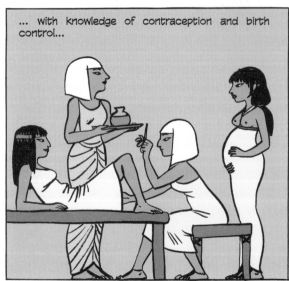

... but also of tender love and eroticism.

In the Beginning was Sex

In ancient Egypt, the very first sexual act has a divine origin — it gives birth to the world and its creatures.

In the beginning was Nun, the dark.

Atum, the first divine power, rises up, born of Nun, the dark, and the primordial ocean.

By masturbating, Atum becomes

RAAAA the sun god.

In Egyptian erotic sculptures, the penis is always very long so that virtually impossible positions can be depicted.

And from his sperm Shu, the masculine principle, god of light, and Tefnut, his twin sister, goddess of moisture, are born.

It is from Tefnut's vagina that the morning dew springs.

WEE WEE WEE! ALL THE WAY HOME

From the incestuous love between Shu and Tefnut, brother and sister, Geb, the earth, and Nut, the celestial vault, are born.

HI MUM!

THOSE KIDS ARE WEIRD...

HI DAD!

Geb and Nut will themselves produce a new generation of gods. Once again, IN THE BEGINNING WAS INCEST!

But the history of the gods does not stop there — it gets even naughtier!

The Story of Osiris
and the Cult of the Phallus

Some great and well-known figures emerge from this petty family history. It is strange, this world of gods where everything that is forbidden to humans is allowed! Taking centre-stage: Isis and Osiris, brother and sister, the children of Gen and Nut. Very soon, they are promised to each other.

It is even said (by Plutarch) that they made love in their mother's belly.

ARE YOU NEARLY FINISHED?

The first king of Egypt, Osiris reigns with his wife and sister Isis, symbol of companionship and ideal of motherhood.

This will not prevent Osiris committing adultery with his other sister, the beautiful Nephthys...

GRRR!!!

Who is by the way his sister-in-law, as she married his brother (his and hers... are you following this?).

Principle of good and of light, Osiris had an enemy: his brother Seth, god of evil and darkness. Jealous of Osiris's radiance, Seth hatches a plot. Persuading his brother to check out a sarcophagus, which is very much to Osiris's taste...

NICE!

Seth shuts his brother inside, and cuts his body into 14 pieces — which he throws into the Nile, scattering them to the will of the waters.

Mad with grief, Isis sets off to search for Osiris's body. Helped by Nephthys, Thoth and Anubis, she finds each part except for his penis, which has been swallowed by a fish.

Hence the taboo forbidding priests from eating fish — an impure food.

According to Egyptian tradition, it is important for the body to be complete in order to be reborn after death. So Isis puts Osiris's body back together, wraps it in bandages, and lastly forms a mock penis from linen strips coated in olive oil.

Then she kneels over him and, using her magic powers, revives the fake phallus by taking it into her mouth; then she couples with the reconstituted mummy to conceive her son, Horus.

And so the cult of Osiris's phallus — a symbol of fertility worshipped all over for its restorative and resurrectional powers — is born.

These are the 3 hieroglyphic phalluses:

VIRILITY

IMPREGNATION

CHILDBIRTH

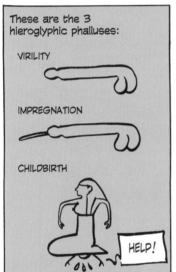

HELP!

During moonlit ceremonies in certain temples, women parade statues of Osiris wielding a very large member that can be moved around with a cord!

For when Osiris died, his soul fled to the moon. And now Seth, still trying to usurp his brother, takes a bite out of it each night — which explains the quarters of the moon.

GRRR

And finally, during funeral services, little obelisks are carved that contain a model, made from canvas and wax, of the deceased's penis, and bearing the wish of a devoted widow:

MAY I MAKE LOVE TO YOU THERE AS WELL.

And on his sarcophagus is written: "Osiris is master of the phallus and deflowerer of women for all eternity."

IT'S DOWN HERE...

Apis the Bull

In Egypt, one of the great misfortunes for a wife is still infertility. Her only recourse: to touch Osiris's phallus or strip naked before the god Apis.

IF I DON'T HAVE TRIPLETS AFTER ALL THIS...

Embodied by a bull, Apis is very carefully selected by priests from the temple in Memphis: the strongest of the bulls, it wears a white triangle on its forehead and is chosen for the potency of its member.

THAT'S ME!

He is transported in procession across Egypt and sails down the Nile on a sacred barge, surrounded by a hundred priests, and acclaimed by the crowds gathered on the riverbanks.

He is then taken to the temple in Memphis...

DO YOU THINK WE'RE GOING TO SEE ELVIS?

... where his only companions are female dancers who show him their sex as a pledge of fertility.

And once a year, to satisfy his sexual urges, he is offered a heifer which is then sacrificed in homage to the god.

IT'S GOOD BEING A BULL!

MAKE THE MOST OF IT BEFORE THEY INVENT BULLFIGHTING.

Along with the cult of Osiris, the cult of the phallus is thus dedicated to Apis-Osiris.

Ramesses II
Pharaoh of Pharaohs

We have now arrived at the reign of Ramesses II, who dominates Europe as much by the longevity of his empire and his turbulent life (he will rule for 67 years and die in 1213 BC at the age of 91) as by the scale of his achievements — political, military, legislative, architectural...

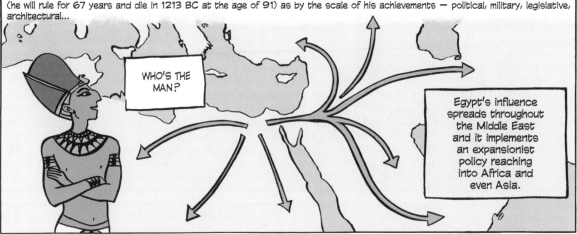

WHO'S THE MAN?

Egypt's influence spreads throughout the Middle East and it implements an expansionist policy reaching into Africa and even Asia.

We are now 1274 BC, in the 5th year of Ramesses II's reign. He has just turned 30 and has raised a powerful army which is advancing through Lebanon and towards Damascus. This is the battle of Kadesh against the Hittites.

Come evening, the generals take stock of the battle.

HOW ARE WE GOING TO COUNT THEM?

DON'T WORRY — I'VE GOT AN IDEA.

They bring the pharaoh the enemies' severed members — the only sure way to tally the dead.

887? THAT SEEMS LOW... COUNT THEM AGAIN TO MAKE SURE.

A force of nature, Ramesses II has a rampant sexual life. Nothing is refused him for he is the equal of the gods. For a start he is married to 12 Great Wives, including Nefertiti, his favourite, who dies aged 48 having given him 10 children.

MY SWEET LOVE...

Overcome with grief, Ramesses will build for her — in the Valley of the Queens — the most beautiful tomb ever discovered.

WHEN I DIE, I HOPE HE BUILDS A TOMB LIKE THAT FOR ME.

NOT A CHANCE, LOVE — SHE WAS HIS FAVOURITE...

Next he marries several foreign princesses — Babylonians, Syrians, Hittites, all daughters of kings and emperors — to form alliances between states.

WHY'S EVERYONE STANDING IN PROFILE HERE?

PFFRT!

He also marries six of his daughters. This is the tradition of royal incest — an often symbolic union designed to retain power.

WILL YOU TAKE YOUR DAUGHTERS BINTANATH, MERITAMEN, NEBETTAWY, ETC... TO BE YOUR WIVES?

Not content with this learned assembly, Ramesses maintains a harem of 200 concubines. According to legend, these wives and concubines will give him over 600 children!

I'M PERFECTLY WILLING TO DO YOUR MAJESTIES' FAMILY TREE BUT, FOR PITY'S SAKE, PLEASE STOP MOVING AROUND ALL THE TIME!

Back to Thebes (now Luxor). The city is buzzing with trade and building work — the New Kingdom is flourishing.

ACCORDING TO IMHOTEP, THE STONES SHOULD BE FINELY CARVED BEFORE BEING PLACED...

Koah, the pharaoh's architect, directs the work on the temple.

Men and women work with him, carving hieroglyphs into the stone.

His wife, Sawertiti, is a doctor.

LADIES FIRST!

Prostitutes (recognizable by their red lips) consult her to avoid becoming pregnant — something their profession doesn't allow them!

AS I TOLD YOU, YOU PUT THIS MIXTURE IN BEFORE MAKING LOVE.*

* The Egyptians used little contraceptive cones filled with pomegranate grains. We know now that these grains naturally contain oestrogen, hence their contraceptive properties.

She shows her a condom made from animal gut!

YOU CAN ASK THE MAN TO PUT THIS MEMBRANE ON.

In the back room, a woman makes a contraceptive tampon by mixing dates, colocynth and honey.

Sawertiti is holding a piece of acacia which she will place in the woman's womb. The Egyptians have already **INVENTED THE COIL!**

A wife consults her to see if she is pregnant.

APPLY THIS PLANT MIXTURE TO YOUR CROTCH — IT CONTAINS BARLEY AND STARCH. IT WILL MIX WITH YOUR URINE. IF THE BARLEY GROWS, IT WILL BE A BOY, IF THE STARCH GROWS IT WILL BE A GIRL. AND IF NOTHING GROWS IT'S BECAUSE YOU'RE NOT PREGNANT.

Life was sweet in ancient Egypt. In matters of gynaecology and in everything to do with fertility, Egyptian physicians' knowledge was very advanced. They were the first to truly understand the roles of men and women in reproduction. Perhaps this is where their egalitarian treatment of women comes from. We can see here that progress towards greater freedom is impossible without an understanding of fertility and without female emancipation — a revolution begun in Egypt but which will take many millennia to take effect.

It's the evening, and Koah and Sawertiti are back home.

I COULDN'T STOP THINKING ABOUT YOU TODAY!

I DREAMED WE WERE EATING AS WE MADE LOVE!*

*a very erotic fantasy at the time!

This image really turns his wife on. She goes off to put on her wig (an erotic touch in readiness for love).

ERR... DARLING, THINK OF YOUR LOVE AND NOTHING ELSE — I'M COMING TO YOU, I'LL BE READY SOON...

WHOA! NEED TO DO SOMETHING ABOUT THAT...

Sawertiti is finely dressed in a linen nightdress, and is wearing mascara, lipstick, jewels and earrings. She strikes up a love song...

MY HEART IS DEVOTED TO YOU...

Koah approaches with affection. He is wearing the "heart scarab" which Sawertiti bought for him.

YOUR DESIRE IS THE FIRE IN MY EYES.

A refined eroticism, tenderness, and devoted affection. They embrace each other, and their limbs intertwine.

YOUR MOUTH IS A LOTUS BUD, YOUR BREASTS ARE APPLES OF LOVE, MY GAZE RISES TO YOUR HAIR AND I AM CAUGHT IN YOUR SNARE.

The next day, Koah and Sawertiti prepare their 10-year-old boy to be circumcised — a traditional ritual that seems to be rooted in Egypt's African origins. We still don't know for certain, however, whether excision was also practised.

CIRCUMCISION is the partial or complete removal of the foreskin. The glans of the penis is thus permanently uncovered. Practised since antiquity, it is still very widespread today: the WHO estimates that there are 600 million circumscribed men in the world.

It is documented in Egyptian sculptures from the third century BC but appears to be even older than this.

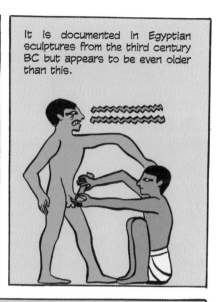

Aside from those rare cases of medical circumcision (eg for phimosis, or tight foreskin) and the recent trend among American hygienists, circumcision is essentially ritualistic and religious. The Brith Milah (covenant), an important ceremony derived from a biblical commandment, is to be carried out without fail on the eighth day of the baby's life.

SNIP!

MAZEL TOV!

Muslim circumcision — "tahara" (purification) — draws from the same source, but is carried out later, between 4 and 12 years old.

THE TRICKY PART IS CATCHING THE KID BEFOREHAND!

In traditional sub-Saharan Africa, where this custom began, it is widely practised regardless of ethnicity or religion, and at very different ages — often as part of a rite of passage to adulthood. There it may be accompanied by the excision of girls.

SNIP!

It has been possible to call EXCISION "female circumcision" because conviction in the equivalence between excision and circumcision is still so persistent. This seems to be rooted in the very widely held belief in a primordial androgyny which subsequently makes it necessary to confirm the sex of each individual. This entails the removal of the female part (the foreskin) from a boy, and the male part (the clitoris) from a girl.

While circumcision continues to be practised without particular harm to men, excision is utterly unacceptable as it involves the sexual mutilation of women, with dire consequences for their genital and sexual health. Excision is disturbingly still very widely practised not just in sub-Saharan Africa but also in the Middle East and Indonesia. It is estimated to affect over 100 million women from 28 countries.

We are in the temple of Isis, goddess of love. Koah and Sawertiti arrive there together. There are singers and dancers everywhere — it's a place of celebration and joy.

Further off, to the side, prostitutes offer themselves in acrobatic positions to say the least!

There are wives among them, for according to ancient tradition every woman in the name of Isis must, once in her life, have sex with a stranger.

Although it is tolerated, homosexuality is seriously frowned upon in an Egypt of conjugal love.

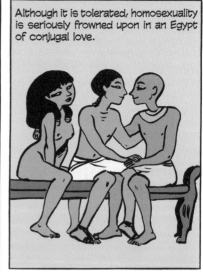

The temple is by the Nile. A huge crowd heads to the riverbank. This is the annual fertility ceremony at which Ramesses II, the pharaoh, masturbates into the water...

To bring power and fertility to Egypt.

Cleopatra
Charm and Sensuality

Dynasties come and go, and first Greece then Rome tighten their grip on Egypt. We are now in 48 BC under the empire of the Ptolemys, Egypt's Greek sovereigns. It's the reign of another important figure...

Cleopatra VII, famous for her nose and her legendary beauty, is remembered today as a powerful woman of exotic charm, a symbol of debauchery and lust. She marries her two brothers, Ptolemy XIII and Ptolemy XIV, one after the other, and becomes Caesar's mistress and Mark Anthony's wife.

They say that in order to meet the great Caesar she had herself delivered to him rolled up in a carpet, which was offered to the emperor and unfurled before him.

She is 21 years old, he is 52. Is it love, or the death by drowning of Cleopatra's husband, Ptolemy, a few months later, that leads Caesar to decide against the annexation of Egypt?

Cleopatra wastes no time in marrying her younger brother, Ptolemy XIV, and becomes the undisputed queen.

Still smitten, the lovers are reunited in Rome, where Cleopatra will spend two years close to Caesar, who will give her a child, Caesarion.

But a misogynistic Roman society disapproves of her...

Four years later, Caesar is assassinated...

Cleopatra returns to Egypt and gets rid of Ptolemy XIV, her brother and husband, by having him assassinated.

She thus becomes the queen mother with young Caesarion, Caesar's son, at her side.

43

This is how Cleopatra will reign, mistress of all she surveys, enjoying her power, and her lovers. She is said to have had wanton feasts where wine and love flowed freely. For her people she is the goddess of love and knows all its secrets. For Rome she is the "queen-whore", mocked for her loose morals.

Cleopatra was known for her irresistible lipstick, made from ants' eggs and ground mealybugs — a bewitching love charm.

And so she came to be known as "Cleopatra Cheilon" ("thick lips"), using her fellatory talent on a hundred of her guards.

TH... THANK YOU, MY QUEEN.

There is no doubt that Cleopatra invented the vibrator — a calabash filled with bees.

IT HAD BETTER NOT POP OPEN...

BZZZ

Emboldened by her powers of seduction, Cleopatra sets off to meet Mark Anthony, leader of the Roman Empire in the east. She arrives at Tarsus on a ship gleaming with gold and with great purple sails...

... and invites Mark Anthony on board for a sumptuous banquet that will set the seal on their love. She is 29, he is 42.

So begins a ten-year affair — a mix of politics and love.

IF YOU LOVED ME, WOULD YOU REALLY ANNEX THIS TERRITORY?

OK, BUT IF YOU LOVED ME, YOU'D HELP ME WITH YOUR ARMY.

They will commit suicide together 10 years later, with Cleopatra stung by an asp brought to her in a basket of figs.

Cleopatra remains one of the most important female figures in history, a woman who knew how to use her charms to meet the demands of love and politics.

CHAPTER 4

GREECE: PANTHEON OF LOVE

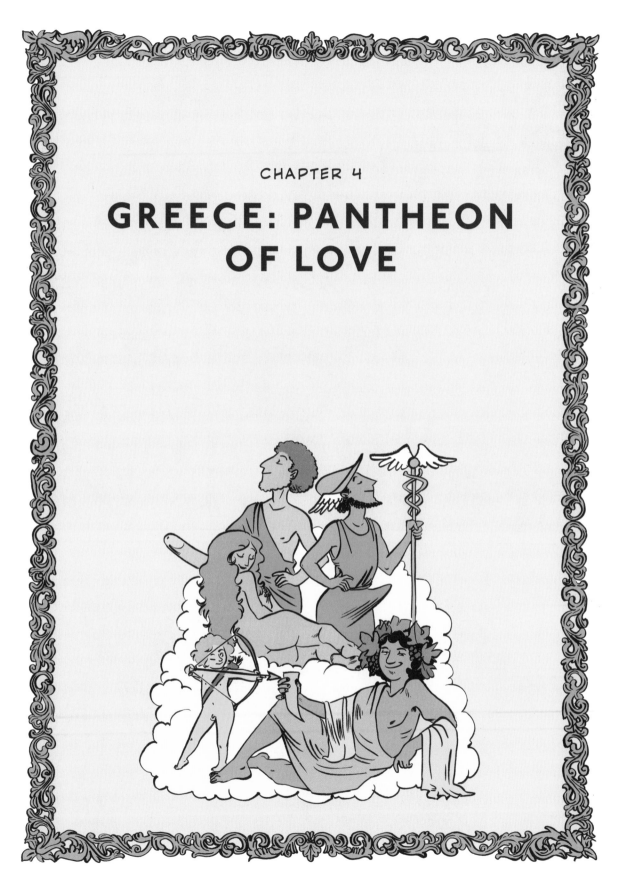

Greece becomes the setting for the pantheon of the gods and legendary heroes who are still with us today, for they have all become part of our vocabulary: Zeus, Aphrodite, Apollo, Hermes, Eros, Dionysus, Priapus, Oedipus, Odysseus, Narcissus...

Some of them are imported — this is true of Aphrodite-Isis-Ishtar...

I'M THE DISHIEST!

MAYBE...

BUT YOU HAVEN'T GOT WINGS!

CHECK AND CHECK!

... and of Hermes and Priapus, both of whom inherit aspects of Osiris and Apis.

In Greece, the gods serve as models and people try to live as they do — which is not always ideal given their idiosyncracies in love.

In the beginning was Chaos, and desire made our world into what it has become.

Then the first two gods appear: Ouranos (the life force) and Gaia (the Earth).

Gaia gives birth in one fell swoop to a horde of extraordinary creatures: the Titans, the Cyclopes, and the Giants. (Warning: gory details!)

YEOW!

OOHH NNOOO!!! Worried by this abundant progeny, Ouranos tries to force them back into their mother's belly.

Gaia, furious, hands one of her sons — the Titan Cronos — a sickle to strike down his father.

FOR YOUR JERK OF A FATHER!

Taking advantage of a moment when Ouranos, erect and about to enter Gaia, is distracted, Cronos cuts off his father's enormous member.

CHOP!

Against all expectations, the blood from the divine phallus drips into Gaia's sex, impregnating her, and all the demons of evil are released...

RE-YEOW!

While Ouranos's member, falling into the Aegean sea, creates a foam from which Aphrodite, goddess of love, majestically springs.

APHRODITE is very beautiful — she is described as Callipygian, meaning "having a very beautiful bottom".

EH! COME AND LOOK!

WOW! SHE REALLY DOES...

A temple is even dedicated to Callipygian Aphrodite, the goddess with the perfect body, and competitions are organized there to find the woman with the most perfect posterior!

Aphrodite is thus worshipped for her powers of seduction and fertility. It is she who awakes nature in spring.

EVERYBODY UP!

IT'S SPRINGTIME!

But she is highly ambivalent: she is both the model wife of her faithful husband, Hephaestus...

... and the insatiable mistress who awakens the passions (she will become the mistress of Hermes, Ares, Adonis...).

ADONIS is the most beautiful being in the world. Aphrodite seduces him.

BIRDS OF A FEATHER...

GRRR

Jealous Ares, her lover and the god of war, transforms himself into a boar that wounds and kills Adonis.

But in the world of the dead, the young god seduces Persephone, Aphrodite's sister.

The two tearful sisters come before Zeus, their father, to complain; he splits the difference...

I CONDEMN YOU TO SPEND HALF THE YEAR WITH ONE, AND THE OTHER HALF WITH THE OTHER.

Adonis couldn't be happier!

Afterwards, a cult is dedicated to him across the world which goes like this: the women who worship Adonis mourn his death each autumn, and wait for the spring to outdo each other in feasting and frolicking.

The symbols of life and death are in place — the rites of the rebirth of nature in spring can now be carried out.

EROS is the god of love, son of Mars and Venus, the most handsome of the young gods. He is depicted as a little boy armed with a bow and arrows

Any man or woman struck by his arrows will fall in love.

HERMES is the son of Zeus and Maia, the mountain nymph (nymphs: divinities who serve as companions to the gods, always ready to make love with them — hence the term "nymphomaniac" to describe an insatiable woman).

He is the messenger of the gods, the guardian of virility — this is why he's always depicted with an erect phallus! He protects travellers and his likeness presides over crossroads, with bearded face and rigid member.

ACCORDING TO THE STATUE IT'S THAT WAY...

Aphrodite became Hermes's lover and gave birth to Hermaphroditus, a being in their own double image, half-man half-woman, their double in name, their double in perfection: a virile member and a magnificent bust.

HIHIHI!

Hermaphrodite thus symbolizes the union of the two sexes, seducing as many men as women. He's a symbol of perfection, combining beauty and virility.

TWICE THE FUN!

CLITORIS was the very beautiful daughter of a Myrmidon (an ant-man), and Zeus fell head over heels in love with her.

WELL DONE, MY LITTLE DOODLEBUG.

She was so beautiful, but so small, that Zeus had to turn himself into an ant to make love to her.

Legendary for her small size, she would lend her name to the tiny organ at the opening of the female sex. "Kleis" in Greek means "the key", the secret to unlocking the vulva, which was named "the door".

NO — IT'S NOT THAT KEY, DEAR.

TIRESIAS was the son of a nymph too. Scaling Mount Cithaeron, he comes across a couple of snakes who are entwined, entangled, embracing.

Frightened by the sight, he separates them and strikes the female with his staff, killing her. The male escapes.

HEEEYAAAAHH!

That very moment he is transformed into a woman. Surprised not to be bothered by the absence of his male member, he nonetheless finds the pair of breasts he has just sprouted rather cumbersome.

He doesn't mind — at last he is going to discover what a woman feels when making love.

YEEEESSSSS

But he is now the keeper of a great secret.

52

Seven years later, Tiresias comes across another couple of snakes. He kills the male, chases the female away, and at that very moment is transformed back into a man — though he doesn't lose any of his memories as a woman.

BLOODY HELL...

This sparks a furious quarrel between Zeus and Hera, his wife, over who feels most pleasure in love — the man or the woman. Zeus insists it's the woman, despite what Hera says.

They summon judges, who don't have a clue.

OH...HMM... IT'S A GOOD QUESTION ... DO YOU KNOW?

PFRT!

So they call Tiresias who has lived as both man and woman. He doesn't hesitate.

THE WOMAN EXPERIENCES TEN TIMES MORE PLEASURE THAN THE MAN.

BOOM!

Furious that women's secret has been revealed, Hera strikes him blind, but Zeus, magnanimously, grants him the power of prophecy to make up for it.

YOU WILL BE A NON-SEEING SEER! TEE HEE HEE!

TEE HEE!

Tiresias, the male-female prophet, thus becomes the famous blind soothsayer of Thebes. He's the one who will warn Oedipus of his tragic destiny.

OEDIPUS, YOU'RE GOING TO FUCK YOUR MOTHER.

And **PRIAPUS**? In one last fling, Aphrodite hooks up with Dionysus, god of wine and love, and becomes pregnant.

But Hera, envious of Aphrodite's beauty, casts a spell on her by touching her belly...

TAKE THAT!

... and has her deliver a deformed child with a gigantic member: Priapus.

Ashamed of this monster, Aphrodite abandons her child and has him raised far away, in Lampsacus.

As a handsome teenager, the god seduces all the ladies of Lampsacus, for whom his deformity is anything but off-putting. But the jealous husbands chase him out of town.

And are punished for it: a cruel disease hits them where it hurts — in the very spot of that divine deformity. They all have "the clap"!

Faced with this epidemic, they consult the oracle, who delivers her judgement.

BRING PRIAPUS BACK AND YOU WILL ALL BE CURED!

He returns to much acclaim and the poor husbands find themselves obliged to worship the very god who stole their wives, to bow down before him and pay him homage.

WOOHOO! PRAISE BE TO PRIAPUS.

WHO'S THE MAN?

PRAISE BE TO PRIAPUS...

PHALLIC FESTIVALS

Several phallic festivals are celebrated in honour of Dionysus every spring, notably on the island of Delos, where enormous stela (or gravestones) represent erect phalluses. These festivals are the great Dionysia, which last for ten days. Two men march at the front of the procession, one carrying a wineskin and the other a vine. A third man pulls along a billy goat, a fourth carries a basket of figs and an enormous phallus brings up the rear.

After the procession the priestesses — or maenads — arrive, dishevelled and possessed.

Then some young virgins, who crown the phallus with flowers and fruit.

The phallophores (carriers of the phallus) wear masks made from acanthus leaves.

Then come the musicians, and finally the ithyphalli, dressed in ladies' robes.

The maenads get drunk, and sip the blood of a freshly killed billy goat, symbol of virility.

These sumptuous festivals are followed by orgies which herald the spring. They also celebrate the grape harvest.

AND WHERE ARE THE WOMEN IN ALL THIS?

In this very rigidly patriarchal society where a man enjoys every right and privilege, the greatest humiliation — for him — is not to have any children, and above all any sons.

But if this man can prove, with the help of witnesses, that it is not a matter of his virility (a friend testifying as to his vigour), his wife is declared infertile and his name is cleared.

> COMPARED TO ME, HE'S VERY VIGOROUS INDEED!

Medical science has already established scientific diagnosis. Hippocrates, the first great physician, has set down the protocol to follow.

> ONE HAS TO MAKE A FIRE OF FRESHLY CUT LEAVES, WHICH CREATES A LOT OF SMOKE.

> THE WOMAN SITS OVER THE FIRE WITH A LARGE BLANKET DRAPED AROUND HER.

> IF THE WAY IS CLEAR, THE SMOKE WILL ESCAPE THROUGH HER WIDE-OPEN MOUTH — FOR THERE IS NO FIRE WITHOUT SMOKE!

> INFERTILE! GO ON, HOP IT! NEXT!

NOTHING

> MY WORD — THEY'RE ALL INFERTILE!

Declared infertile, this woman has only one hope: Priapus. She makes sacrifices, follows the processions, takes part in the orgies...

... and, miracle of miracles, nine months later...

> YOU SEE, DARLING!

These very permissive festivals, during which women cut loose, are in marked contrast to daily life, where wives are barred from the male world, confined to the home, and the sight of other men's members would be regarded as profoundly indecent.

EEEEEEEK!

One particular place is forbidden to them: the gymnasium, where men work out naked (gymnos = naked) and cultivate the virile values that demonstrate male supremacy and beauty. It is a place of highly eroticized masculinity, a place of body worship and pederasty where lovers can meet.

LOVE, HOMOSEXUALITY AND PEDERASTY

Love is not a unique notion to the Greeks, who distinguish between:

PHILIA: friendship and mutual respect with someone of the same sex.

EROS: sexual desire and attraction.

AGAPE: selfless and unconditional love.

STORGE: filial and familial love.

  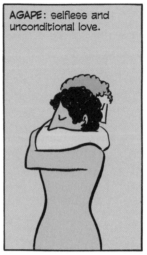 

These different kinds of attachment form complex relations between individuals (men or women) that are distinct from what we call "sexual orientation" today — something which, for us, is dominated by the idea of sexual attraction. Sexual practices are thus experienced separately from these ties of affection.

It is difficult for us to comprehend the sexual practices of antiquity and to describe them using today's terms. The Greeks were neither "homosexuals" nor "heterosexuals": they did not distinguish between homo-, bi-, or heterosexuality — these words would have made no sense to them.

Particularly as these terms are 19th century inventions.

YOU ARE EXHIBITING HOMOSEXUAL BEHAVIOUR!

I BEG YOUR PARDON?

What's more, approval or condemnation of sexual behaviours varies from city to city (Athens, Sparta, Thebes...) and changes over time.

NO! SPARTANS DO NOT LOOK "GAY"!

In this very markedly misogynistic society, all that matters are the terms of domination: a man is a superior being because he is capable of penetration. He — or she — who is penetrated is inherently inferior.
It doesn't make much difference who is penetrated...

whether it's a woman (a naturally inferior being)

a young boy (in pederasty)

a prostitute

a sexual slave

The only thing that counts is the attraction this man feels, for a man can have sex with anyone he likes, but preferably someone "beautiful".

HA HA HA! THEY SAID SOMEONE BEAUTIFUL!

YES — SHE'S BEAUTIFUL ON THE INSIDE!

58

Homosexuality, as the word is understood today, is very rare in Classical Greece. It is often condemned because, paradoxically, ancient Greek society is in some ways "homophobic" — it doesn't accept the idea of an enduring relationship between two men.

AND SOMETHING TELLS ME WE HAVEN'T SEEN THE LAST OF THAT HOMOPHOBIC CRAP...

POOFS

In Athens, homosexual prostitutes and transvestites are held in contempt, as men are not meant to make themselves effeminate — and therefore inferior — in any way.

AND TO TOP IT ALL HE'S DRESSED LIKE A CHICK!

LOOK WHO'S TALKING!

For the fate of each man is first and foremost to marry and have children. As this marriage is a family arrangement, it is never about a romantic bond between husband and wife.

The man may thus enter into an intimate but short-lived pedagogic relationship with an adolescent — known as "pederasty".

FATHER, MOTHER — NOW THAT I'M MARRIED I'M GOING TO BECOME A PEDERAST.

THAT'S AS IT SHOULD BE, MY BOY!

Pederasty, in Athens, is a pedagogic relationship according to which a young married man — a citizen of the city — initiates a prepubescent boy into social life and into sexual intimacy to make a "citizen" of him. It is in a sense a rite of passage to adulthood and to citizenship. It is important to remember that this rite of pederasty was confined at first to certain aristocratic circles, then spread to the middle classes — it was not practised by everyone.

The "lover" (erastes) is a young man of about thirty. He chooses his "beloved" (eromonos) for his beauty and youthfulness.

NOPE...

NOPE...

NOT MUCH OF A CHOICE...

The beloved is about 12 years old but beardless above all. It's the lack of hairiness that determines the attraction.

WHOA! ... YOU'RE GOING TO FIND IT TRICKY!

BUT I'VE GOT A HORMONAL IMBALANCE!

The lover devotes all his time and effort to make his beloved a "good citizen". In return, his beloved offers himself sexually to his lover — who is always in an active role. Fellatio, intercrural sex (between the thighs), sodomy...

ONCE I'VE SODOMIZED YOU, YOU'LL BE A GOOD CITIZEN.

GREAT. IS THAT ALWAYS HOW IT WORKS?

The lover is proud of his beloved — he publically declares his love for him and this is respected.

THIS IS MY PROTÉGÉ!

CLAP CLAP

At the same time, it would be awkward if this lover were to be drawn to another adult, as love between men was considered unworthy of an honourable citizen.

THIS IS MY PROTÉGÉ.

EEEWW! YUCK!

POOFS!

This pederastic relationship is short-lived, however — it ends after a few years when the boy's body hair starts to grow.

THAT'S IT! I'VE GOT HAIRS! I'M A CITIZEN NOW!

And later, once he is married, this young citizen will become a lover and initiate a handsome ephebe himself.

THE SYMPOSIUM

We are in 5th century Athens, 404 BC, the heyday of Classical Greece — the age of philosophers and of the Republic.

Plato, Socrates, and a few followers such as Noademes, walk the streets as they philosophize — which is why they are known as "peripaticians".

The same term is used for prostitutes — for they too walk the streets as they philosophize.

Socrates strolls a little behind the group, his head in the clouds.

SOCRATES IS BY FAR THE WISEST OF MEN FOR HE DOESN'T THINK HE KNOWS WHAT HE DOESN'T KNOW.

MY DEAR PLATO, IF WE KNEW EVERYTHING THERE WOULD BE NO POINT IN LEARNING.

IGNORANCE OPENS THE DOOR TO KNOWLEDGE.

LET'S MEET THIS EVENING FOR A BANQUET AT AGATHON'S HOUSE.

I'LL COME WITH ACHILLES.

We shall follow Noademes through the streets of Athens. By the port of Piraeus, he passes by a brothel, and eyes up a man and woman who try to lure him in.

FOR A MEASLY OBOL — TREAT YOURSELF.

To appease the ardour of young Athenians, Solon has created municipal brothels supervised by civil servants. Women bought by the state work there for pitiful sums. Through this law of "public utility", pleasure become accessible to all.

civil servant

Noademes returns home to his wife, Sawfia. Surrounded by maids, Sawfia organizes the house, looks after the four children, and bows before Noademes.

WELCOME HOME.

In Greece the situation for women not is not particularly enviable. When they are 15 years old their father chooses a husband for them, then they must submit to their husband's will and be absolutely faithful. Men, on the other hand, are free to pursue sex with concubines, slaves, prostitutes or even a relationship with a young ephebe. There is no place for love in marriage!

I'VE JUST SCREWED TWO PROSTITUTES AND NOW I'M HEADING OFF WITH ACHILLES TO AGATHON'S BANQUET.

SEE YOU TOMORROW.

FAB! HAVE A GREAT NIGHT, DARLING.

Noademes leaves and meets up with Achilles, his beloved.

They make their way to Agathon's house, where the banquet is taking place.

Plato's famous *Symposium* (banquet) gave rise to one of the most celebrated definitions of love. Around a large table the meal is served. Noademes and Achilles take their places along with Phaedrus, Plato, Pausanias, Socrates and Aristophanes.

Phaedrus Is the first to speak.

> ISN'T IT STRANGE THAT NO POET HAS EVER PAID TRIBUTE TO LOVE, EVEN THOUGH HE IS SUCH A GREAT GOD?

> I PROPOSE FOR THIS EVENING THAT WE EACH DELIVER TO OUR BEST ABILITIES A SPEECH IN PRAISE OF LOVE.

There is no greater god than Love. Of all the gods he is the one who does man most good. An army comprising only lovers and their beloved partners could thus conquer the whole world. Only lovers know how to die for each other.

> HANDS OFF MY BOYFRIEND!

> GRRRR!

Next it's Pausanias's turn:

There is not one love but two: Celestial Love and Common Love. I say the common lover who loves the body rather than the soul is lecherous. Only he who loves for virtue is truly beautiful.

> YOU'RE THE MOST BEAUTIFUL

Aristophanes gets up:

In the beginning, human beings were different to today. There were three kinds...

Males, females, and androgynes.

They had four arms, four legs, two faces opposite each other on the same head, four ears and two sexes.

As they had the audacity to compare themselves to the gods, Zeus separated them in two to punish them

Ever since, they have only had two arms and two legs, one face and one sex.

Each of us is therefore only a half of our whole being, and one half is always searching for the other! Love restores us to our true nature: "two beings together as one".

This story explains sexual attraction between men, between men and women, between women, and even adultery, as union with an androgyne half.

Socrates is the last to rise:

> IN ORDER TO DESIRE, MAN MUST LACK THE VERY THING HE DESIRES. LOVE IS THE LOVE OF SOMETHING HE LACKS. AND THAT SOMETHING IS LOVE.

> HELL, YEAH!

> BRAVO!

> YOU'RE ON FIRE, SOCRATES!

They shower each other with praise for these fine declarations when all of a sudden they are interrupted by a horde of drunken revellers led by a lady playing the flute.

> YOU PUT YOUR LEFT LEG IN...

> FANCY A DRINK WITH ME?

And the banquet turns into a drinking session which knocks them out until dawn.

AND WHERE ARE THE WOMEN IN ALL THIS?
PART TWO

Towards the end of the 5th century BC, the women of Athens rebel against their husbands' indifference.

As adultery is very severely punished, some of them have relationships with other women. Female homosexuality, for the Greeks, is of no significance and is therefore not worthy of condemnation.

BY THE WAY, DEAR — THIS IS CALLIOPE, MY BELOVED.

YEAH, YEAH. DELIGHTED I'M SURE...

Famous on her island of Lesbos, the poet Sappho sings its praises:

MY PASSION FOR THE BEAUTY OF WOMEN, CHANGING LIKE SUMMER SUNSETS, DRIVES THE WAVES AND THE FLAMES...

And throughout the long war between Sparta and Athens, the deserted women of Athens console themselves by ordering from Miletus, in Asia Minor, the very latest thing: an "olisbos". It's made of leather, packed with wool, and in the shape of a male member.

It's the first sign of defiance by women who dare to face up to their husbands by asserting they no longer depend on them for their lives or their loves. Aspasia, the companion of Pericles, master of Athens, led this first movement towards female emancipation.

Confronted with these unacceptable and "abnormal" behaviours, one man believes that a lack of sexual satisfaction has made these women ill. Hippocrates thus provides a detailed diagram of this illness he calls "hysteria":

THE UTERUS IS THE WOMAN'S VITAL ORGAN. IF IT IS NOT SUFFICIENTLY IMPREGNATED WITH SPERM, THE BLOOD IS FORCED UPWARDS, AND THIS CAUSES ANXIETY AND NERVOUSNESS. ONCE SHE MARRIES THE ILLNESS WILL DISAPPEAR.

This idea will dominate medicine until the 20th century!

A few years after this attempt at female emancipation, the most renowned of Plato's pupils — Aristotle — will vociferously condemn this rebellion by asserting, once and for all, the "natural superiority" of man over woman:

HEAT IS ENERGY BUT THE WOMAN IS COLDER THAN THE MAN — A SIGN OF HER INFERIORITY... SHE IS AN INCOMPLETE MALE, AN INFERIOR BEING.

ELEMENTARY, MY DEAR PLATO! IT IS MAN, THROUGH HIS SACRED SPERM, WHO PERPETUATES THE SPECIES!

LOGICAL!

His misogynistic judgement was gospel in the West until the 18th century!

THANKS, ARISTOTLE!

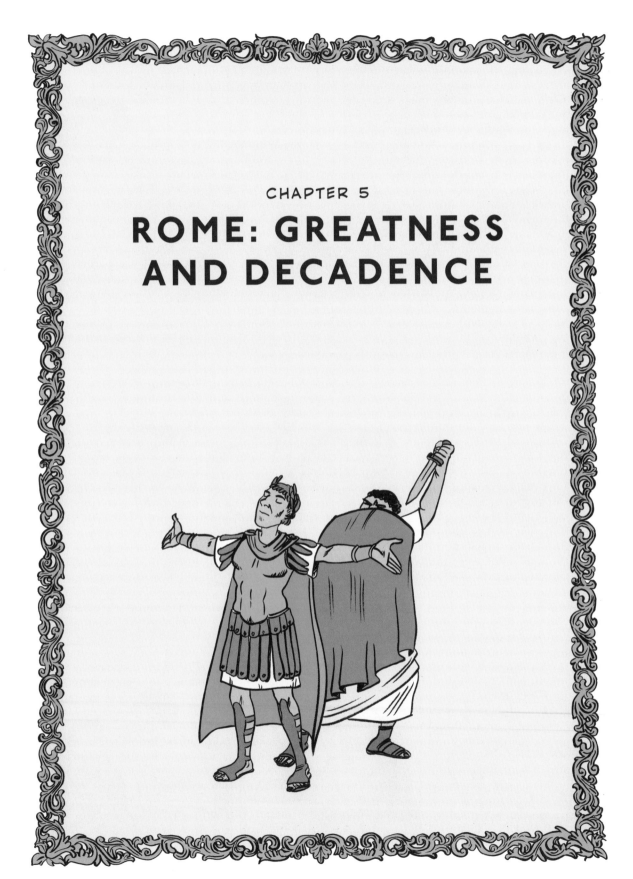

CHAPTER 5
ROME: GREATNESS AND DECADENCE

Rome — the opportunist — borrows its beliefs and its gods from all of antiquity. The Greek Pantheon is thus reborn with new names: Zeus becomes Jupiter, Aphrodite Venus, Dionysus Bacchus, and Greek orgies become Roman orgies — to such an extent that in Rome the expression "to live like Greeks" means to live freely.

I'VE GOT A STRONG FEELING OF DÉJÀ VU...

Rome is founded by Romulus and Remus in 753 BC in a territory dominated by the Etruscans for the first two hundred years.

A seagoing people from what is now Tuscany, the Etruscans allow women a great deal of freedom. They take part in weddings and banquets just like their husbands.

They even do gymnastics with them — or with female friends. For the men, there is nothing shocking about seeing these women naked.

AVE

AVE

According to Theopompus, the Greek historian, they have their fun with men in complete freedom, and are not afraid of having sex in public!

Uni, goddess of love, even encourages women into sacred prostitution.

WHICH DOESN'T MAKE THEM SAINTS!

Aside from mistresses, men have their way with young boys and adolescents, just like in neighbouring Greece.

YOU STILL LIVING WITH YOUR PARENTS?

ER, YEAH.

In 509 BC, Rome banishes the Etruscan tyrant, installs the Republic and establishes a repressive new order. Love — free or in public — is no longer acceptable.

THAT'S ENOUGH OF THAT CRAP!

Marriage is the basis of social stability, and of the orderly life of the city. The man is the head of the family, and the woman no longer has a place in public life.

THAT'S ENOUGH OF THAT CRAP!

And finally, adultery is roundly condemned.

THAT'S ENOUGH OF THAT CRAP!

Roman society is rigidly patriarchal, organised around masculine ideals, domination, and self-discipline. The adult male can do as he pleases as long as he retains his position of superiority.

SAME TOGAS, SAME BATTLE!

WE SEE EYE TO EYE!

ROMAN

GREEK

But he cannot be attracted to a young citizen. There is no pederastic tradition in Rome. Another important difference with Greece: the shamefulness of nudity, a symbol of disgrace.

COVER THAT PHALLUS THAT I CANNOT BEAR TO SEE!

?

Homosexuality is accepted if the citizen retains the active role — whether with a prostitute or a slave. However, any behaviour which is effeminate, receptive or passive, is denounced — and will often be used as an insult in the political sphere.

MY LORD CONSUL, ALLOW ME TO SAY THAT YOU ARE A HOMOSEXUAL!

OOOH! OOOOH!

As the woman is naturally inferior, her place is in the gynaeceum. Her virtues are modesty and chastity.

I SCREW WHOEVER I WANT. I'M A SEX BOMB.

RIGHT, THAT'S ENOUGH OF THAT CRAP!

A few centuries later, with the expansion of the Empire, Roman customs become more relaxed. However, one still has to decide which god to worship — a laborious task in the celestial muddle that clutters up Roman life.

Each god is invoked for his particular virtues:

Jupiter is the guarantor of oaths.

CAESAR — YOU SHALL HAVE GAUL!

SNIGGER!

Juno protects matrons.

FEAR NOT — I AM PROTECTING YOU.

GREAT — THANKS!

Vulcan, the home.

WATCH OUT WITH THAT HAMMER, THOUGH...

Lucina, periods.

YOU'RE THE BEST! YOU'VE SAVED MY LIFE.

Mutinus, fertility, and Priapus, virility.

CLEOPATRA — YOU WILL BEAR CAESAR'S CHILD.

CAESAR — YOU SHALL HAVE GAUL.

SNIGGER!

In his *Satyricon*, Petronius tells of the shame his impotent hero feels: "My body was no longer bringing me satisfaction when I met Oenothea. She made a fake penis out of leather, coated it in oil and ground pepper before slowly introducing it up my anus.

She rubbed my testicles with the same mixture then thrashed me below the navel with a bunch of nettles. This is how I recovered all my strength."

An aphrodisiac at last!

Ovid recommended another stimulant: "The right testicle freshly cut from a donkey, and soaked in wine. It's excellent!"

THE LEFT ONE, ON THE OTHER HAND - YUCK!

ROMAN FESTIVALS

And so the festivals multiply to celebrate Liber, Bacchus, Flora, Priapus... and along with these come excesses, and even orgies. In the Roman year there are over a hundred days given over to festivals; almost half are devoted to gods of fertility, fruitfulness, and loose morals.

From 27 April to 2 May, the Floralia (in honour of the goddess Flora) celebrate the flowering of spring - five nights of hunting and dancing in the valleys and gardens around Rome. Women appear naked on stage and perform obscene dances.

At the Lupercalia, devoted to the protector of fields and herds, priests flog women with leather whips to keep the wolves away from the pastures. The whip excites desire and sensuality, proofs of fertility.

At the Saturnalia, seven days and seven nights are just about enough to celebrate the sowing season. Men and women drink at the same table and share the same bed. There is no holding back — happiness comes from reckless abandon.

Each year on 17 March, the start of spring, the Liberalia take place: great rural festivals in honour of Liber, god of fertile pastures, of vines and of wine — so named because wine liberates the soul.

THAT'SH TREW!

As the centuries pass, the cult of Liber takes on even greater importance under the name of Bacchus, imported from the Greek Dionysia. As time goes by, the Bacchanalia degenerate into feasting and carousing, opening the way to all sorts of excess, all sorts of violence and even murder.

In Rome, the Bacchanalia inspire nocturnal orgies which cause public disorder. Women, disguised as Bacchante, run riot along the banks of the Tiber, initiating themselves into the mysteries of Bacchus.

SHAME ON THEM!

THEY'RE COMPLETELY PISSED!

Consequently, in 186 BC, fearing a sectarian plot, the Roman Senate bans all orgiastic festivals.

THE BACCHANALIA ARE TO BE ABOLISHED WITHIN 10 DAYS.

THAT'S ENOUGH OF THAT CRAP!

OOOOH...

FOLLOWERS OF BACCHUS WILL BE IMPRISONED OR BANISHED, AND MORE THAN 7000 CONSPIRATORS CONDEMNED TO DEATH.

DON'T WORRY — WE'RE FULL.

ERO!

The cult will be banned for over a century until Caesar allows it once again.

GO ON — KNOCK YOURSELVES OUT!

YIPPEEE!

DAILY LIFE IN ROME AND THE ART OF LOVE

We are in Rome in 1 BC.

Nonus is a young tribune, an officer in the legion. As he does every morning, he is devoting his time to military activities with his friend Marcus.

> I'M WARNING YOU, MY DEAR MYRMIDON...

> AT THE END OF THE BALLAD COMES THE BLOW!

Towards noon, he goes to the baths to relax and recuperate among men. The baths are never mixed.

Afterwards, Marcus heads to the lupanar.* The phallus over the door gives it away. There are several lupanars in Rome, where prostitution is legal.

*The lupanar takes its name from the wolf (lupus), for the women who work there are she-wolves!

Nonus hesitates, and hangs back.

> GO ON — COME INSIDE! IF YOU DON'T, YOU'LL END UP DOING SOMETHING DODGY WITH YOUR WIFE.

> O FEET, O LEGS, O THIGHS! HOW I WOULD LOVE TO DIE FOR YOU.

> O BOTTOMS, O SHOULDERS, O VAGINAS! I AM WILD ABOUT YOU!

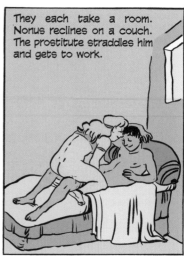

They each take a room. Nonus reclines on a couch. The prostitute straddles him and gets to work.

Later that afternoon they leave the lupanar to attend a banquet, where slaves wait on them. They drink wine mixed with honey or watered down — never neat...

Only alcoholics drink wine neat.

ALCO!

?

Marcus strokes a slave's bottom.

YOUR MEMBER'S SWELLING AND THERE'S A SLAVE AT YOUR DISPOSAL — DON'T HOLD BACK!

Nonus grabs a slave for himself...

... and kisses him all around his mouth.

THESE KISSES FEEL SO GOOD.

The pinnacle of pleasure for Romans is a kiss on the skin, especially around the mouth ... But never near the genitals. Performing cunnilingus would be most insulting for a man.

YOU WANT ME TO KISS THAT!? YOU PERVERT!

To accept an offer of fellatio would be even more shameful, as it's only good for old men!

NOT WHILE I'M ALIVE!

WE'LL HAVE ANOTHER CHAT IN A FEW YEARS...

In Rome, everyone makes fun of impotent old men because, as in all traditional societies, the mouth and the genitals are never meant to meet.

AND AFTERWARDS YOU KISS YOUR CHILDREN WITH THAT MOUTH!?

In the evening, Nonus returns home to Sawbina and their son. Starting in the doorway, the house is filled with protective symbols. Little phalluses called "fascina" protect the home. A large tintinnabulum — a kind of mobile with bells and a phallus — hangs in the hallway.

I BANGED MY HEAD ON THE TINTINNABULUM AGAIN...

OUCH — NOT COOL!

Around the necks of Sawbina and her son hangs another little phallus ("mutinus") to ward off evil spells and ensure good health and prosperity for this young child.

SAY "DADDY"!

PHALLUS!

Nonus and Sawbina find some privacy and make offerings at a little domestic altar devoted to Mutinus.

As usual, Sawbina lies back and thinks of Rome as her husband joylessly deposits his sperm.

BASICALLY, I'M DOING THE STARFISH...

A free woman, a self-respecting Roman citizen, is taught to experience no pleasure. She is destined to reproduce — which is why she is called "the belly". This is how to make children who will become "good citizens"! This ordained wifely "passivity" will serve as a model for the West for almost 2000 years.

YOU'D BETTER BE A GOOD CITIZEN!

'CAUSE I'M REALLY BORED IN BED!

This contrasts with the "activism" of the prostitute who, unlike the wife, is active and on top!

YEE-HA!

Some wives even sue husbands who try to enjoy sex with them. They accuse them of uxoriosis, of desiring their wife's body, and can have them punished on these grounds. A respectable mother is no whore!

HE... HE TRIED TO TOUCH MY BREAST!

JUDG

No feelings either: "To love one's wife is shameful. One must behave like a husband not a lover" (Senecus).

AH! I DON'T LOVE YOU!

ME NEITHER, PUMPKIN

This year in Rome, Ovid has just written *The Art of Love*. Sawbina props herself up in bed and caresses Nonus, who turns round in shock.

WHAT ARE YOU DOING, SAWBINA?

PURR PURR

This guide for lovers is revolutionary because it is also addressed to Roman women. Each woman must get to know herself to find which way she prefers to make love.

IT'S OVID WHO'S TEACHING US THE ART OF LOVE.

In his book are all the ways of making love — the 90 positions according to Ovid — but there is above all a new, egalitarian vision of lovemaking: "in love, the two sexes are equal and pleasure must be shared equitably. Yes, love must be a shared reward and not a selfish satisfaction. Nor should it be a duty."

SO MAYBE NOW WE CAN HAVE A LITTLE FUN FOR A CHANGE!

Nonus and Sawbina make love like lovers — a novelty for husbands and wives in imperial Rome.

Fearing that Rome's women will rebel against, and dominate, its men, Augustus condemns Ovid to an exile from which he will never return, for all his pleas.

SCRAM!

I'LL TAKE CARE OF THAT, BOSS!

Throughout this long history of sexual freedom, one can see that any progress is swiftly followed by a period of repression.

ONE STEP FORWARD...

TWO STEPS BACK...

DECADENCE

The years that follow show the decadence of Roman customs.

Caligula is renowned for his cruelty, violence, and debauchery. He proclaims himself "emperor of vice".

He respects no limits in his sexual excesses, enjoying sexual relations with his three sisters, Drusilla, Agrippina and Livilla...

CALIGULA! LEAVE YOUR SISTERS ALONE!

Having several homosexual relationships with young boys — something which was always frowned upon in Rome...

AND BY THE YOUNG BOYS TOO...

Setting up a lupanar in his palace and prostituting the senators' wives.

Caligula revels in executions and torture before he is assassinated himself, at the age of 28, by his guards.

—PHEW!

Claudius, who succeeds him, is the only Roman emperor to be strictly heterosexual and fairly moderate in sexual matters.

His wife, Messalina, makes up for this weakness. Renowned for her wantonness and her nymphomania, she prostitutes herself in Rome's lupanars and at her famous orgies.

ER... HAVE YOU NEARLY FINISHED, DARLING? I'D QUITE LIKE TO GO TO BED.

Claudius, with no child of his own, leaves the throne to his son-in-law, Nero, that bloodthirsty emperor.

I KNOW YOU'LL BE A GOOD EMPEROR.

DON'T WORRY — I'M GOING TO SET THE PLACE ON FIRE!

A proconsul at 15, emperor at 17, Nero is already married to his half-sister Octavia, Claudius's daughter, by the time he has his brother-in-law, Britannicus, assassinated...

FIRST THE FATHER AND NOW THE BROTHER — DEATH BY POISON IS BECOMING A FAMILY TRADITION!

NICE!

AGRIPPINE

Abuses his mother and has her assassinated...

STRIKE MY BELLY!

He kills his second wife, Poppaea, with a kick to the belly while she is pregnant.

IT'S A FAMILY TRADITION!

WE STRIKE THE BELLY!

He then marries Statilia Messalina, and a year later Sporus, his young favourite — whom he castrates before marrying.

OUCH

Nero knows no limit in his perversions. He prostitutes himself, covered in animal hide, then abandons himself to his freedman, Doryphoros, for whom he takes the woman's role.

MOOOORRRE DORYPHOOORE!

Forced to commit suicide, Nero stabs himself at the age of 31. With him the Julio-Claudian dynasty — a particularly deviant and decadent one — comes to an end.

PHEW!

We are now in the first century AD: 24 August 79. Decadent Rome heads south for its pleasures, to the shores of the Tyrrhenian Sea, and the seaside towns of Herculaneum and Pompeii.

Pompeii is the capital of well-being. Signs of luxury and pleasure abound. Symbol of prosperity, the phallus is venerated as a protective god.

HIC HABITAT FELICITAS

In the side streets, there are several lupanars between the shops.

Today the Vetii, wealthy shopkeepers, are holding a large party at home. The master of the house and his guests, freedmen and women, prostitutes, or even slaves, indulge in the pleasures of love.

CARPE DIEM!

BRRRM

The Christians, still clandestine, are the first to denounce the decadence of the Empire.

IT'S NO LESS THAN DIVINE JUSTICE!

THE BEGINNINGS OF CHRISTIANITY

In the early days of the Christian era, Rome opens up to a new faith. Its emperors convert and the Empire endures another five centuries of armed conflicts and compromises with corrupt and debauched popes. The Gospel is the new Bible.

Although the only part of Saint Paul's Gospel anyone remembers is a speech advocating strictness and chastity, he is in fact the only one to speak openly about sexuality.

PERVERT!

His *Letter to the Corinthians* offers a message of decency, asking the faithful to renounce debauchery and corruption at a time when Corinth had more than 10 000 prostitutes.

BROTHERS, DO NOT FOLLOW THE DESIRES OF THE FLESH. LUST, IDOLATRY, LECHERY, ORGIES, DRUNKENNESS TAKE YOU AWAY FROM GOD'S KINGDOM!

HEY!

HE'S STEALING OUR CUSTOMERS!

But he is also a messenger of Christ with a new doctrine: man should be "the husband of one woman only".

WE HAVE A PROBLEM.

In his *Letter to the Ephesians*, he adds a very modern message: "Husbands, love your wives as Christ loves his Church."

HOW WAS IT FOR YOU?

However, Paul will be remembered for another sentence instead: "The husband is the head of the wife as also Christ is the head of the Church", which will legitimize male domination until the 20th century.

GET DOWN ON YOUR KNEES AND PRAY FOR ME!

In the 3rd and 4th centuries, the first Christian marriages were conducted in secret, sometimes in a forest at night, between two fiancés blessed by a priest and confirming their consent. A great novelty: this marriage, which entails mutual consent, imposes a strict and indissoluble monogamy.

BY THE WAY, I FORGOT TO TELL YOU, DEAR — I'M PREGNANT WITH YOUR BROTHER'S CHILD!

I'VE CHANGED MY MIND...

TOO LATE.

But eventually the families react and, a few centuries later, insist that this ceremony should be public, and devise impediments to marriage: mistaken identity, consanguinity (even to the 20th degree), union with an infidel, or someone who's already married, or mad, or impotent... in such cases marriage is considered null.

YOU'RE ACCUSING MY FIANCÉ OF IMPOTENCE AND ADULTERY, BUT MUM... HOW DO YOU KNOW?

YES, GOOD POINT — HOW DO YOU KNOW?

ER...

CHAPTER 6

THE MIDDLE AGES: HEAVEN AND HELL

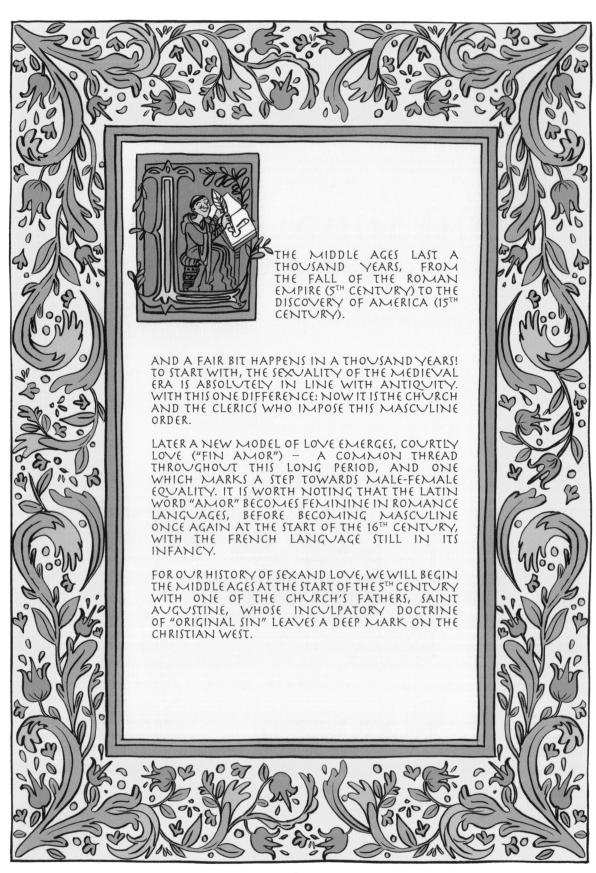

THE MIDDLE AGES LAST A THOUSAND YEARS, FROM THE FALL OF THE ROMAN EMPIRE (5TH CENTURY) TO THE DISCOVERY OF AMERICA (15TH CENTURY).

AND A FAIR BIT HAPPENS IN A THOUSAND YEARS! TO START WITH, THE SEXUALITY OF THE MEDIEVAL ERA IS ABSOLUTELY IN LINE WITH ANTIQUITY. WITH THIS ONE DIFFERENCE: NOW IT IS THE CHURCH AND THE CLERICS WHO IMPOSE THIS MASCULINE ORDER.

LATER A NEW MODEL OF LOVE EMERGES, COURTLY LOVE ("FIN AMOR") — A COMMON THREAD THROUGHOUT THIS LONG PERIOD, AND ONE WHICH MARKS A STEP TOWARDS MALE-FEMALE EQUALITY. IT IS WORTH NOTING THAT THE LATIN WORD "AMOR" BECOMES FEMININE IN ROMANCE LANGUAGES, BEFORE BECOMING MASCULINE ONCE AGAIN AT THE START OF THE 16TH CENTURY, WITH THE FRENCH LANGUAGE STILL IN ITS INFANCY.

FOR OUR HISTORY OF SEX AND LOVE, WE WILL BEGIN THE MIDDLE AGES AT THE START OF THE 5TH CENTURY WITH ONE OF THE CHURCH'S FATHERS, SAINT AUGUSTINE, WHOSE INCULPATORY DOCTRINE OF "ORIGINAL SIN" LEAVES A DEEP MARK ON THE CHRISTIAN WEST.

SAINT AUGUSTINE

Augustine is born in 354 in Numidia, now Algeria, to a very unfaithful father and a Christian Berber mother.

His childhood is marked by transgression — "the simple pleasure of doing what is forbidden", he says in his *Confessions*.

COME ON! LET'S NICK THE PEARS!

WICKED! WE'RE JUST BONKERS!

He then lives together with a woman for a long time and, at the same age as Christ (33 years old), he converts, becoming a "eunuch for God" and later a bishop.

FORGIVE ME FOR THOSE PEARS, O LORD.

I SWEAR, I WON'T SCREW ANYMORE.

By the time of his death, he leaves behind a considerable œuvre of theology and philosophy which passes on a very pessimistic conception of the body as enemy of the soul.

AND YOUUU... MUST... NOT... SCRREEEW.

Feeling he is at the mercy of his sexual impulses, Augustine flagellates himself so as to renounce the flesh, and to attain an ideal of chastity and abstinence.

VADE RETRO, VILE SLUT!

Sensuality is the source of sin, whether it is a matter of acts, thoughts or desires. Only conjugal, procreative sex is permitted — with no place for desire.

HOW ABOUT PROCREATING THEN?

MY DARLING, YOU REALLY ARE MOST PROVOCATIVE!

In the same tradition as Aristotle's misogynistic outlook, the thought of Saint Augustine will hold sway for centuries to come.

HOORAY! THANK YOU, SAINT AUGUSTINE!

BETWEEN WAR AND PEACE

From the 5th to the 10th centuries in Europe, men and women are buffeted by many conflicts, by endless wars between the pretenders to various kingdoms, and by severely straitened material circumstances — particularly for women struggling to stay healthy and look after children whose survival is anything but certain.

The men are absent — away at war, or on their travels... One pregnancy soon follows another, on average every 16 months.

WITH A HUSBAND AWAY FOR 15 MONTHS...

30 to 40% of new-borns die before the age of 1, and 60% before the age of 20.

MUMMY! WHAT'S THAT?

I DON'T KNOW, DEAR, I'VE NEVER SEEN ONE BEFORE!

A couple's life together on average lasts 8 years. Women are often widowed very young, their husband killed at war or, from the 11th century, during the Crusades.

YOUR HUSBAND PERISHED DURING THE ASSAULT.

SO SOON? BUT HE DIDN'T EVEN MANAGE NINE MONTHS!

As for the men, they would often lose their wives in childbirth.

SHE DIDN'T EVEN MANAGE NINE MONTHS.

SHE DID JUST.

The family is at the heart of society. A young girl has no say, particularly among the nobility, who hold all the property and all the power. To ensure the handing down of inheritances, marriages are arranged and decided by the families.

HE'S THE HEIR OF THE COMTE D'ANJOU — SO SHUT IT!

Once again, the duty of fidelity is utterly one-sided: adulterous women are condemned to death, usually by drowning...

YOU BROKE MY HEART, FAYE!

BUT HE CHEATED ON ME TOO — WITH THAT MARGAUX!

While unfaithful husbands face no punishment — other than a modest fine.

AND DON'T LET ME CATCH YOU AGAIN, EH?

NO CHANCE! NOW I'M A WIDOWER I'M GOING TO MARRY MARGAUX!

TEMPTATIONS

To prevent any prenuptial temptations, most girls of noble birth spend a few years in a convent.

They then devote themselves completely to their "lord and master".

As for the priests, they often live with women or visit prostitutes, especially from the 11th century onwards, when priests are no longer allowed to marry.

LET'S GO TO CONFESSION, MY CHILD.

JUST LIKE THAT? WHAT ABOUT SOME FOREPLAY?

But as the husband is often away, and as everyone has urges, most women find a kindly soul in the form of their confessor.

ALL YOU HAVE TO DO IS SEPARATE SPIRITUAL LOVE AND CARNAL DESIRE — IT'S NOT COMPLICATED!

THIS IS SPIRITUAL LOVE.

EXACTLY

These affairs are kept absolutely secret for fear of "flagrante delicto" — a synonym for being condemned to death with one's lover.

LOOK HOW DEVOUT THEY ARE!

COME ON, GIRLS! LET'S HEAD FOR THE CONFESSIONAL FOR A BIT OF "OUR FATHER"!

HiHiHiHi

HiHiHi

HiHiHi

Among the humbler social classes, prenuptial sexual relations are not condemned to the same extent as long as the young couple involved are "promised" to each other. However, an unwanted pregnancy can always mean a death sentence for a woman.

BUT WE'RE GETTING MARRIED NEXT WEEK!

Medieval fables, which are often pornographic, tell us how the men of the people screwed, snogged, took their women Turkish style... The same goes for the monasteries and convents, where urges are hard to contain.

AND DELIVER US FROM EEEEEVIL!

AMEN!

Among the nobility, husband and wife spend little time together and don't share their emotions.

THIS HOUR SPENT WITH YOU HAS BEEN PERFECTLY NEUTRAL.

AM I BOTHERED?

Moments of intimacy are governed by very strict religious values: all sources of excitement must be avoided, all excesses, all nudity, all sensuality...

EASY! EASY!

... and frequent sex, which can make for a "slippery womb" like a prostitute's — the reason why they don't have children!

WELL I NEVER!

And in any case everyone knows that self-abuse shortens one's life — one orgasm is the same as two bleedings.

PHWOOOAARR! COME ON YOU RASCALS!

Under the Carolingians, from the 8th to the 10th centuries, the Church recommends 250 days of abstinence to avoid "arousing the wrath of God".

YES, BUT IS THAT IN TOTAL, OR IN A ROW? 'CAUSE IF IT'S IN TOTAL THAT'S TWICE A WEEK, WHICH I CAN HANDLE!

As the sexual act is for procreation only, the clergy imposes the "missionary position" —regarded as natural in that it places the woman in an inferior position. The other positions — such as "cowgirl" (*Andromaque*) or "doggy style" (*levrette*) are strictly forbidden as they risk provoking the wrath of God.

WE DON'T WANT ANY CRAP!

The marriage must remain chaste: "the man who loves his wife with too much ardour," Saint Augustine tells us, "may be charged with adultery!"

ALDEBERT — IT'S TOO GOOD WITH YOU.

SOMETIMES, I'M NOT EVEN SURE I WANT TO TAKE A LOVER.

VIRGINITY

Before becoming a virtue, virginity was a necessity. The theologians all agree: a woman without virtue is a woman lost.

And women are separated into three categories: virgins will have a hundred times their just desserts; widows sixty times; and wives thirty.

> AND VIRGIN WIDOWS, A THOUSAND TIMES!

Concubines and prostitutes are fallen women.

In the 12th and 13th centuries, a turning point in the Middle Ages, the fascination with the model of virginity is absolute — inspired by the image of Christ's mother, who remained pure her whole life.

> HMM... WELL ACTUALLY SHE PULLED A FAST ONE ON JOSEPH!

Throughout her childhood, a girl is exhorted to protect her "jewel" — the honour of her family depends on it. The day she marries, the "seal" must be "intact". Her wedding thus resembles a sacrificial episode, as the young virgin is delivered to her all-powerful master.

> OYEZ ! THE SEAL IS INTACT!

In the 12th century, the split between the education of boys and girls becomes very marked: girls remain cloistered within the domestic sphere in service of God and family, not going to school or to university; boys are allowed freedom of movement and of thought. Whether they are peasants, merchants, or knights — they have every reason to leave home and travel.

The principal concern for women at this time is to protect their virginity, then their chastity, either in marriage or in religious orders.

For the nuns, the slightest weakness would be a rift in their marriage with Christ, a grave sin bringing shame on the whole Church.

> BUT LOOK, I'VE FOUND THE ANSWER!

The convents and the monasteries multiply, evidence of the sanctuary which guilty girls, repudiated wives or the many widows are all seeking far from male desires.

> ASYLUM! MERCY! OTHERWISE WE'RE SO GOING TO GET SCREWED!

It is important to note that the vast majority of women regard the inferior status to which they must submit as normal. They are the first to teach this to their children.

> AND THE PRINCE MARRIED THE PRINCESS. BUT WHEN HE REALIZED SHE WAS NO LONGER A VIRGIN, HE REPUDIATED HER AND BURNED HER AT THE STAKE! THE END!

> SOMETHING TELLS ME THAT WE'RE NOT ALWAYS GOING TO HAVE IT EASY...

LOVE STORIES

Faced with all these prohibitions, only the powerful can allow themselves amorous adventures.

This is the case for Robert the Pious, son of Hugues Capet, and king of France in 987. After four years of marriage, the young Robert (now 19) repudiates Suzanne (35), whom his father had forced him to marry, and takes off with his cousin Bertha — who, to top it all, is already married herself.

CLEAR OFF, YOU OLD HAG!

BAM

The two lovers make no secret of it, and even find an accommodating bishop to marry them.

I NOW PRONOUNCE YOU SECOND-HAND MAN AND WIFE.

However, Pope Gregory V declares their union "incestuous", condemns them to seven years of penance and excommunication if they fail to separate!

YOU'RE GOING TO BURN IN HELL WITH YOUR SUCCUBUS!

WOAH! WELL IF YOU PUT IT LIKE THAT...

A hereditary passion: his grandson Philippe I, married to Bertha of Holland, falls head over heels for Bertrade de Montfort, wife of Fulk d'Anjou.

YooHoo!

In his passion, and using all his power, he repudiates Bertha and marries Bertrade.

BAM

Two years later, the bishops at the council of Autun excommunicate the royal couple who, despite the Church's anathemas, remain together.

PAF

Pope Urban II comes to France to excommunicate the king, and forbids him from taking part in the Crusades.

NO CRUSADING!

HUH!

Even among royalty, the Church remains all-powerful in its sway over marriages, families and private lives.

TWO MYTHS

THE CHASTITY BELT

Contrary to popular belief this belt was not invented in the Middle Ages to guarantee a wife's chastity while the husband was away during the Crusades, but later, in the Renaissance.

Jealous husbands, afraid their young wives would be unfaithful, inflicted this armoured purity on them.

IT'S GOING TO BE REALLY PRACTICAL FOR GOING TO THE TOILET!

But it's above all in the 19th century, when medievalism is rife, that this myth is invented and that these contraptions are used... in brothels! These days they are common in BDSM.

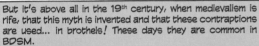

WHAT DOES "LOST THE KEY" MEAN TO YOU?

THE "DROIT DE SEIGNEUR" (or "DROIT DE CUISSAGE")

I'LL BRING HER BACK TOMORROW!

It's a very widely held notion according to which, in the Middle Ages, every Lord would have "jus primae noctis" (the right of the first night) over the girls or wives of his serfs and servants — as if he were on a par with God.

A milder version — the "droit de jambage" (or right to the leg) — would have involved the Lord symbolically sliding his leg between the bodies of the young couple to bless their union.

OY! THEY SAID THE LEG!

In truth, no historian has ever uncovered any mention of this practice in the public archives, or in common law. On the contrary, what have been found are condemnations of some Lords for exploiting their position to commit sexual abuse.

CRUSADES, COURTLY LOVE AND LOVE COURTS

The first crusade, 15 000 to 20 000 strong, leaves for Jerusalem on 15 August 1096.

Many will not return.

WE ARE THE FIRST CRUSADERS AND NOTHING'S GOING TO SAVE US

This is the age of the first love songs, warbled first by the troubadours (in Occitania) then by the trouvères (in northern France).

I AM LEAVING, MY LADY... I KNOW NOT IF THOU SHALT EVER SEE MY RETURN...

At the heart of courtly love ("fin amor" or "perfect love") is the woman — the object of all desires. This is a veritable revolution.

The lady is sovereign, the knight is her vassal. Society's medieval values are turned upside down — this haughty figure is unapproachable, her lover worships at her feet.

To win her favours, he submits to trials of love: in the case of the *asag*, he has to stay chaste throughout a whole night spent beside his beloved — the two of them naked. The amorous knight tosses and turns between euphoria and despair.

YOOHOO!

WHAAAAT A BUMMMMER...

Here are a few examples of the courtly code that has to be followed: jealousy makes love blossom.

AND MURDEROUS IMPULSES.

Tormented by love, the lover sleeps little and eats less.

YOU LOOK IN SPLENDID SHAPE, MY LOVE!

THANKS TO YOU, MY SWEET!

Love and lust don't go hand in hand.

THEY DO SOMETIMES!

Sawanette du Buis, daughter of the comte de Provence, is the wife of Bertrand, vicomte d'Avignon, and presides over the first Court of Love held in Pierrefeu.

Noam Régnier is a young knight who has earned his spurs with Bertrand d'Avignon. He is as loyal to his Lord as he is to Sawanette, his beloved, the mistress of this Court of Love, who pretends not to notice him.

She opens the session...

GENTLE LADIES, COURTLY KNIGHTS, TROUBADOURS, JONGLEURS, WE ARE HERE TOGETHER OF OUR OWN FREE WILL TO FIND ANSWERS TO LOVE'S QUESTIONS.

THE ONE WHICH CONCERNS US TODAY: IS LOVE BETWEEEN HUSBAND AND WIFE POSSIBLE?

Fanette de Beaux and Hugonne de Sabran launch into great diatribes. Each woman has her say.

TOTALLY!

OBVIOUSLY!

At the end of the debate, Sawanette reads out the verdict.

OUR JUDGEMENT MUST BE ACCEPTED AS GOSPEL...

WE JUDGE LOVE BETWEEN MARRIED COUPLES TO BE IMPOSSIBLE.

It therefore follows that the constant presence of one's spouse is incompatible with the objective of perfect love: desire.

 The court disperses, damsels and knights converse by a grove. Encounters happen as if by chance...

... in a bedroom...

... or an alcove...

There is nothing chaste about these: courtly love is adulterous, privileging erotic desire, the exploration of sensuality...

... and for women, the clitoral orgasm scorned in marriage.

YEESSSSSS!

But this courtly love remains the reserve of a very restrictive aristocratic sphere, and does little to soften the brutality and crudeness of knights and their usual manners.

NEXT TIME YOU COULD AT LEAST TAKE YOUR ARMOUR OFF!

HÉLOÏSE AND ABELARD
OR THE TEACHER AND THE STUDENT

Courtly love was a new way to treat women. There are many stories that describe this new love; perhaps the best example is that of Héloïse and Abelard.

In 1113, Pierre Abelard is one of the most famous Christian theologians.

HE'S CHAAASTE!

HE'S SOOO CHASTE!

This is why he's chosen by Canon Fulbert to be tutor to his beautiful niece, Héloïse. It's love at first sight.

Rumours abound, but Fulbert refuses to believe them.

BACK THERE HÉLOÏSE IS DOING SOMETHING FILTHY WITH ABELARD!

IMPOSSIBLE – HE'S SOO CHASTE!

Passion consumes the lovers and Héloïse eventually becomes pregnant.

Abelard steals her away and takes her to Brittany, where their son, Astralabe, is born. They marry in secret.

SHHHHH...

Mad with rage, Fulbert denounces Abelard for betraying the Church and, with some accomplices, has him castrated.

OW OW OW

Héloïse takes the veil and becomes an abbess. Abelard becomes a monk. But rather than fade, their passion inspires some of the most beautiful love letters of all time.

OW

ON BROTHELS AND SAINTS

In the Middle Ages prostitution is generally accepted.

"To pay for coming, is to come without sinning", they used to say.

PAY UP FRONT — THEN YOU CAN RELAX.

For the virtue of prostitutes is that they protect respectable women from their husbands' brutal passions.

YOU LIKE THAT, HUH! YOU HUSSY! SAY IT — SAY YOU LIKE IT!

WELL FOR THE LAST TWO HOURS, NOT SO MUCH...

And she is also a source of revenue for the municipalities, seigneuries and even monasteries which sometimes own brothels.

YEEESSS!

WAHEEY!

WOOHOO!

WE SHOULD NEVER HAVE PUT THE PROSTITUTES NEXT TO THE CHAPEL...

Pope Sixtus IV himself acquires a brothel to fill the coffers of the Vatican — and to build the Sistine chapel to which he gives his name.

AND ALL THAT THANKS TO WHORES.

In response, Saint Louis bans prostitution throughout his kingdom in 1254.

THAT'S ENOUGH OF THAT CRAP!

Two years later, the uproar this causes leads him to regulate it instead, obliging whores to ply their trade outside town. So they set themselves up in wooden barracks called *bordes* (boarded houses), hence the name of *bordels* (brothels). And in Paris, they are *au bord de l'eau* (by the river)!

THIS ONE'S EMPTY — IT'S THE ONLY ONE THAT'S NOT SHAKING.

In the Middle Ages, abbeys and chateaux own bath-houses. These public baths in the town are frequented by both sexes. They are generally houses of ill-repute run by courtesans. There are often two to a bath. Out of coquetry ladies keep their hats on and wear necklaces! In his *Decameron*, Boccaccio dishes the dirt on these brothels: "You are courteously welcomed, a young girl bathes you, massaging you with her gentle hands. Then she finds you a bed, and an alluring young woman takes care of you."

Despite the Church's attempts to ban and suppress these havens for orgies, the vogue for "group baths" will last for almost two centuries.

The 13th century is also the century of Saint Thomas Aquinas, an enemy of pleasure and sexuality.

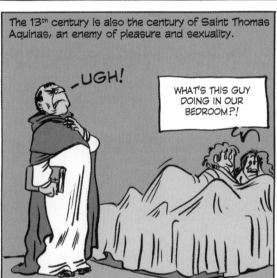

-UGH!

WHAT'S THIS GUY DOING IN OUR BEDROOM?!

He perpetuates the misogynistic views of Aristotle and Saint Augustine by reaffirming that woman is an incomplete being...

AN UNFINISHED CREATURE! A CHILD!

WHOA THERE! JUST A TAD FRUSTRATED ARE WE?

... a being in need of a guardian!

SAINT THOMAS SAID SO!

CLASSY!

As for homosexuality, relatively accepted until now, he condemns it: it is the gravest of all the sins of the flesh. It is a perversion close to cannibalism, and an insult to God!

AAAAH! SATANAS! VADE RETRO!

WE'VE REALLY GOT TO STOP THIS GUY FROM BARGING INTO BEDROOMS!

The Middle Ages, which seemed close to breaking the hold of male domination, end with the revival of the Inquisition.

JOAN,
MAID OR WITCH?

Joan is 17 years old, the daughter of Jacques d'Arc, a rich farmer from Domrémy in Lorraine.

Joan is very devout and for years she has been hearing celestial voices in her father's garden, and in particular the Archangel Saint Michael who calls on her to liberate the kingdom from its English occupiers.

GOD WOULD LIKE YOU TO SEND THE ENGLISH PACKING — GET IT?

At the time a prophecy is doing the rounds in Lorraine that a maid will save the kingdom of France.

AND SO APPARENTLY A MAID IS GOING TO SAVE THE KINGDOM! WELL I NEVER!

WELL, IT WON'T BE ME!

NOR ME!

Joan is taken before Robert de Baudricourt, captain of Vaucouleurs. After hesitating a great deal, Baudricourt gives her an escort of six men who will remain loyal to her.

AS FOR YOU BOYS, SHE STAYS A MAID ALRIGHT! SO HANDS OFF!

Joan sets off to join the campaign, wearing men's clothes and sporting the "bowl cut" of the men of the time.

In Chinon she meets the Dauphin and predicts the liberation of Orléans, his coronation in Reims, and the liberation of Paris.

CAREFUL, SIRE — SHE MAY BE A WITCH.

THAT'S A GIRL?

IT'S THE ARCHANGEL SAINT MICHAEL WHO TOLD ME!

This matters. Virginity is at the time seen as a talisman against which the devil has no defence. If Joan is a maid, she cannot be a witch! They also have to check she is not a man — a job for the matrons, the midwives of the age.

SHE'S A GENUINE MAID!

SHE IS WHOLE!

AND SHE'S NOT A BLOKE!

Reassured, Charles places Joan in charge of a convoy of provisions which she takes to Orléans.

After saving Orléans, and after Charles VII's coronation in Reims, Joan heads off to war again but is captured by the Burgundians, who sell her to the English.

THAT'S A GIRL?

A year later she is tried for heresy. The accuser, Bishop Cauchon, claims that the voices are really the work of the Devil. He tries to paint her as a witch and demands a fresh inspection of her virginity...

CAUCHON BY NAME..!

THIS WITCH IS WEARING MANDRAKE OVER HER HEART!

... which is proved once again!

SHE'S A GENUINE MAID!

AND SHE'S NOT A BLOKE!

SHE IS WHOLE!

Finding no grounds for an indictment, the tribunal finds her guilty of lies, apostasy, blasphemy — in a word, of being a witch.

DEATH!

BUT... BUT...

Joan is condemned to be burnt alive at the Place du Vieux-Marché in Rouen on 30 May 1431. She is 19 years old.

DIE, SLUT!

THAT'S A GIRL?

A second trial, in 1456, declares Joan's innocence and thus completely exonerates her 25 years after her death.

LOOK, JOAN! THEY'VE CONFIRMED YOUR INNOCENCE AT LAST!

A FAT LOT OF GOOD THAT DOES ME!

THE DEVIL AND WITCHES

The devil is the bearer of evil and of sex, but above all of evil through sex. He thus plays an important role as challenger to God, and inspires the holy terror of evil. Over the centuries, this fallen angel is transformed into a master of debauchery.

The devil is responsible for all sexual abominations. His sex is double, allowing him to penetrate the vagina and the anus at the same time. His sperm is icy!

The punishment of lust is depicted everywhere. On the modillions of Romanesque churches women are wrapped up by serpents devouring their crotch, their breasts, even their vagina — the parts where they commit sins.

FENG-SHUI!

In the 15th century, the devil is a bogeyman for the people, and thousands of women believe they are in congress with him. Dreams of sex with the devil become an obsession.

OH, SATAN! YESSS! SATAAAN!

WHO'S THIS SATAN?

The number of supposed witches multiplies and the judges of the Inquisition gather extravagant confessions...

I WAS FLYING THROUGH THE AIR, STRADDLING A BROOM, TO MAKE IT TO THE WITCHES' SABBATH...

TO... TO THE STAKE!

From the 15th to 16th centuries, the judges of the Inquisition interrogate those they call "the brazen slaves of Satan". Their interrogations, focussed on sex, aim to describe the devil's sexual parts and the ways the accused have fornicated with him.

AND THE DEMON? WHAT WAS HE LIKE?

HIS SPERM — WAS IT HOT OR COLD?

AND HIS MEMBER — WHAT WAS IT LIKE?

HE WAS A VERY DARK MAN WHO TOLD ME I HAD TO GIVE MYSELF TO HIM.

IT WAS COLD, I REMEMBER.

TWISTED, IN THE SHAPE OF A SERPENT. I SUFFERED GREATLY.

This woman told the truth — she endured the devil's member and its icy sperm. She is acquitted.

But not all interrogations are this straightforward...

—AAARGH!

OK! OK! I FORNICATED WITH THE DEMON! BUT HAVE PITY — UNTIE ME!

IT WORKS REALLY WELL THIS WITCH-DETECTOR!

TOTALLY! THEY ALL CONFESS!

Witches, convicted of heresy and of being in league with the devil, are at best condemned to perpetual imprisonment, or at worst to death for having "made love to the Devil".

For the three centuries the Inquisition lasted in Europe, there were an estimated 100 000 sorcery trials and 50 000 executions.

CHAPTER 7

THE RENAISSANCE: THE ARTIST AND HIS MODEL

The Renaissance begins in Italy in the 14th century and spreads across Europe in the 16th century. It is first of all a cultural and intellectual revolution, born of the rediscovery of antiquity, which sweeps away a thousand years of medieval barbarism and places man at the centre of the universe — leading to the rise of humanism. It is also a fabulous age of discovery — Gutenberg invents the printing press around 1450, Christopher Columbus discovers America in 1492 — and a period of religious reform: Luther and Calvin lived in the 16th century.

In the history of love, the Renaissance marks the end of the kind of male friendship that had prevailed since antiquity, and the true beginning of marriages of love among the people and emerging bourgeoisie.

DO YOU MIND BEING ONLY MY SECOND BEST FRIEND?

While the nobility persists with arranged marriages.

IT'S NOT ALL ROSY, HAVING A BIT OF CASH...

With this marriage of sentiment, which brings together desire and conjugal ties, heterosexuality lays down the law. This creates a split with a homosexuality that still has no name.

The Church condemns "sodomies", meaning acts contrary to nature, including anal penetration...

SODOMY!

...but also all those non-procreative erotic practises: fellatio, cunnilingus...

SODOMY!

And masturbation counts as sodomy too...

SODOMY!

MICHEL DE MONTAIGNE

Since antiquity, friendship between men has been rooted in male domination without constituting homosexuality as we understand it today. This friendship, which is a genuine form of companionship, can range from shared pleasures and female prey to the eroticization of male relationships. Michel de Montaigne, writer and philosopher, is the last and greatest example of this.

In 1558 he meets Étienne de la Boétie. They are both magistrates at the Bordeaux Courts of Justice. They are 25 and 28 respectively and begin a legendary, loving friendship which will last five years...

YOU'RE MY BEST MATE, YOU ARE!

MY BESTEST EVER MATE!

... until the death of La Boétie in 1563.

WAAAAAAH!

LIFE IS NOW JUST SMOKE AND DARK NIGHT. WE SHARED EVERYTHING — HE WAS DEARER TO ME THAN LIFE ITSELF, AND I WILL ALWAYS LOVE HIM.

Two years later, Montaigne marries Françoise de la Chassaigne who will give him six daughters, but this is the nobility and for Montaigne, "marriage is a cage, its birds desperate to escape".

HAPPY FAMILY

He will go further still: "a good marriage rejects the conditions of love (...) no wife would want to take the place of her husband's mistress." (*Essays* III,5)

SHALL WE MAKE LOVE, DEAR?

ARE YOU NUTS? MAY I REMIND YOU WE'RE MARRIED!

Montaigne retreats to his tower for the remainder of his life and begins writing his *Essays*, which are published in 1580. There he speaks of the profound bond he shared with La Boétie...

THE ATTACHMENT OF ONE MAN FOR ANOTHER IS IN ITSELF NEITHER GOOD NOR BAD...

YEAH, RIGHT – 'ERE'S YOUR DINNER-TRAY, MISTER MONTAIGNE.

... such as this very famous maxim:

"IF YOU PRESS ME TO TELL YOU WHY I LOVED HIM: BECAUSE HE WAS HE, BECAUSE I WAS I".

Montaigne will be one of the first to say openly that homosexual love is a love like any other.

GALLANT LADIES

In the same period, Brantôme describes the beginning of female liberties in love.

"No beautiful woman, once she has played the game of love, ever unlearns it."

IT'S LIKE RIDING A BIKE — YOU NEVER FORGET.

AND YOUR ANACHRONISMS, DARLING?

It reflects the persistence of the masculine order, by which every man dominates the women he "possesses"...

GRRR...

MINE!

... but also the first feminist protests: in his *Life of Gallant Women*, Brantôme describes the rebellion of certain women of the nobility who no longer tolerate this domination.

DOWN WITH PHALLOCRATIC TYRANNY!

"I have heard tell of a very beautiful and respectable lady... so proud that she refused to allow her husband to mount her... she always wanted to be on top.

SMACK!

I'M NOT A DONKEY!

For love, she chose her equals or her inferiors... so that, whether standing...

She said that should her husband ever ask whether such and such a person had made love to her, she could always swear, without offending God, that he had never mounted her!"

.... or sitting...

... or lying down, her lovers could never make her submit! This lady always wanted to have the upper hand and make her man submit to her.

ADULTERY AND MARRIAGES OF LOVE

In the Renaissance, the "companions" — those men who live among men, away from their wives...

...progressively disappear to make way for the "companionable wife" and the model of the "good husband".

However, the sensual dimension of marriage begins to worry the confessors, who attempt to suppress conjugal eroticism.

This new marriage of love inevitably comes with other joys to complicate matters — jealousy, suspicion, adultery, cuckoldry...

It is worth noting that, as usual, adultery is always female! For, despite the progress of marriages of love, male domination remains intact, and an adulterous man is never condemned.

On the other hand, a man dominated by his wife loses his authority — he's no longer a man! That's why everyone points the finger at cuckolds.

They are mocked in songs...

BLOW HIM UP THE ARSE, I WILL BLOW YOU,
I WILL BLOW YOU
BLOW HIM UP THE ARSE, HE'S BEEN TAKEN FOR A RIDE!

THEY'RE SO SWEET!

ADORABLE...

IT'S YOU THEY'RE TALKING ABOUT.

... and at popular festivals, such as "the donkey ride": the cuckolded or battered husband, his arse in the air, rides backward on the donkey holding it by the tail, sometimes led by his own wife, in a procession through the town.

Adultery is also punished as part of popular rituals. This is the sentence known as "the race": the condemned couple, the wife and her lover, have to run naked through the village. In some regions the wife pulls her partner along with a rope attached to his private parts.

NOT SO FAST!

THAT'S WHAT SHE SAID!

It is worth noting of course that none of this applies to the nobility, who never wash their dirty linen in public.

ARTISTIC REVOLUTION

Newly liberated bodies appear in art, sculpture and literature. The art of the Renaissance is an art of the sexual body.

Drawing on the cult of the Madonna, this new sensibility shows the extent to which women have a right to beauty and love.

Artists vie with each other to do justice to feminine charms. Nudity becomes a source of inspiration for Botticelli, Cranach, Raphael, Rubens...

JUST FOR PAINTING SOME NAKED CHICKS...

THAT'S QUITE A CROWD!

OH, COME ON!

The ideal woman begins to emerge, a woman of flesh and desire. Noah the Venetian, a pupil of Titian's, adds the finishing touch to the *Venus d'Urbino*.

Maria Saw, his model, is a very beautiful young woman, lying completely naked on a bed. Not knowing where to put her hand, she places it discreetly over that most intimate place. The great artists paint nudes in a way that was forbidden during the Middle Ages.

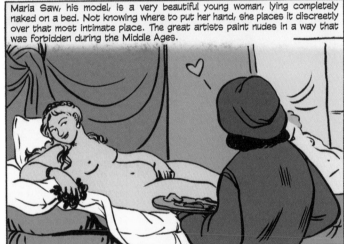

For the Church, however, art is sinful in its exhibitionism. A few centuries earlier, to look at a woman's naked breasts was a mortal sin.

AAARGH! A HALF-NAKED MADONNA! AAARGH!

WHOOPS!

AGNES SOREL

At the court of King Charles VII, dresses are already so open that women cover up their nipples with make-up.

STILL AGNES SOREL

OH MY WORD! JUST AS WELL I ALWAYS HAVE MY MAKE-UP WITH ME!

A century later measures are taken regarding all this over-the-top cleavage among women of the nobility such as Gabrielle d'Estrées and her sister.

COVER THIS BREAST I CANNOT BEAR TO SEE!

LOL!

THE HENRYS
Young favourites and old charmers

As ever, the nobility and royalty can indulge in excesses forbidden to the people.

Henry III is born in 1551. He is the fourth son of Catherine de' Medici, He falls madly in love with Maria of Cleves...

... the fiancée of the Prince de Condé, whom she marries.

In September 1574, Henry, now king of France, tries to have Maria's marriage annulled so he can marry her.

BUT... SHE'S MINE!

I'M THE KING — I CAN DO WHAT I WANT!

Two months later, he learns of her death.

Inconsolable, Henry surrounds himself with his "mignons" or favourites, and no longer shows any interest in women. Or so the story goes for a king everyone knows was "homosexual".

Not true! This rumour is spread by the protestant preachers, who are opposed to all frivolity, and who are the first to denounce the favourites as homosexuals.

POOFS AND DANDIES! POOFS IN WEIRD CLOTHES!

HAVE YOU SEEN YOURSELF?

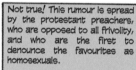

Brantôme refers to the "mignons de couchette", or "bedroom favourites", who have the honour of spending a night in the royal bedchamber. A way for the king to reward a loyal servant — a custom far older than Henry's reign.

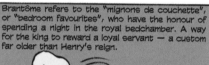
The King's Pyjama Parties

The favourites powder themselves, apply make-up, curl their hair, wear lace, earrings, and large, starched ruffs. They will be the source of a great deal of ridicule because of their effeminate habits.

IGNORE THEM — THEY'RE JUST JEALOUS.

HAHAHAHA!

But there is nothing to suggest the supposed homosexuality of the sovereign, who had many mistresses.

ERR... SORRY, SIRE.

I'M STILL HERE... YESTERDAY'S PYJAMA PARTY AND ALL THAT...

There's certainly no debate about Henry IV, the Béarnais, a colourful hedonist, connoisseur of good food and beautiful women. Nicknamed the "Vert-Galant" ("old charmer") for his ardour with his mistresses, he's a horny devil despite his age. He is known to have had 73 official ones, and they give him 22 children while at court.

From the daughter of his gardener from Nérac, Fleurette, with whom he fell in love when he was 18...

... to Queen Margot's ladies of honour...

YOU COULD AT LEAST WAIT 'TIL THE END OF THE CEREMONY, HENRY!

... to Gabrielle d'Estrées, his greatest love.

I HATE IT WHEN YOU DO THAT!

Anything goes for the Gascon: the peasant...

... the bourgeoise...

... the marquise...

... his cousin...

... a nun...

... or a prostitute...

The moment he spots a woman he fancies, Henry dismounts with panache...

... and has his way with her on the ground, against a wall, in a stable...

HMM... THIS MIGHT TAKE A WHILE!

In his defence, he says — no doubt apocryphally — of his member:

UNTIL THE AGE OF 40...

I THOUGHT IT WAS A BONE!

LEONARDO, MICHELANGELO AND SEX

Leonardo da Vinci is one of the great minds of the Renaissance, the very model of a humanist artist, painter, sculptor, engineer, architect, philosopher, writer... His *Mona Lisa* is one of the masterpieces of Western art.

HE'S ALSO THE ONE WHO INSPIRED THE CHARACTER OF BATMAN!

What is less well known is that he is one of the leading anatomists of the 15th century, carrying out several autopsies to deepen his knowledge of the human body — the better to paint it. Leonardo observes, dissects, sketches and makes discoveries that are ahead of their time.

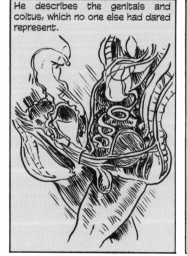

He is the first to undertake the anatomy of the foetus and of pregnant women.

HOW DID THAT GET IN THERE?

He describes the genitals and coitus, which no one else had dared represent.

Seen as "unworthy" at the time, these parts are still today labelled "shameful" in some anatomy textbooks.

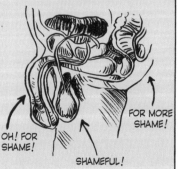

OH! FOR SHAME!

FOR MORE SHAME!

SHAMEFUL!

And he's also the one who discovers the mechanism of erections...

... under the influence of desire, the penis fills with blood, whereas everyone since Aristotle had thought it filled with air from the lungs!

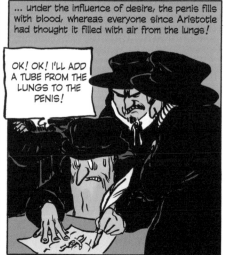

OK! OK! I'LL ADD A TUBE FROM THE LUNGS TO THE PENIS!

Freud will say that Leonardo da Vinci sublimated his homosexual urges in his art, a case of Freud repressing and projecting his own homosexuality no doubt.

YOU CAN CLEARLY SEE THE DRESS IS A VULTURE WHICH BRUSHES AGAINST THE CHILD'S MOUTH WITH ITS TAIL!

Leonardo and Michelangelo both maintained virile friendships throughout their whole lives, like many men of their time, and lived a homosexual existence that was concealed for many years.

At the start of the Renaissance, and above all in Italy, the love of boys returns to the fore in literature, painting and sculpture, before the severe repression of the Enlightenment begins.

Clothes emphasize masculine charms. They hug the thighs, mould the buttocks, bulge around the crotch, and accentuate the shoulders and waist.

This exaltation of the male body is particularly vivid in the case of Michelangelo, whose passions consume both his art and life.

TEEHEE! GOD'S BUTTOCKS!

When he is 24 years old, and already a famous painter, Leonardo is accused — mistakenly it seems — of "active sodomy", and imprisoned.

AND IF IT HAD BEEN PASSIVE, IT WOULD HAVE BEEN THE DEATH PENALTY!

He is then, and for the rest of his life, the lover of young ephebes: first Salai then Francesco Melzi.

MY MUSES...

Michelangelo surrounds himself with young boys — assistants, models, or bedroom companions...

WHO ARE YOU MEANT TO BE?

THE VIRGIN MARY.

... then, and for the rest of his days, he lives out an enduring romance with Tommaso del Cavalieri, a young noble from Rome who dreams of being an architect...

IT'S FABULOUS! YOU ARE THE SHINING LIGHT OF OUR CENTURY, MY SWEET GENIUS.

If Leonardo and Michelangelo are not harassed, they owe this to their great fame.

THE CONDOM

The previous century had ended with the return of Christopher Columbus's sailors in 1493.

Along with their other things, they also brought back syphilis.

COOEEY! I'M SYPHILIS! YOUR FRIEND FOR LIFE!

The controversial origins of syphilis have recently been cleared up by Kristin Harper at the University of Atlanta: her genetic study has shown that the strains of treponema (the cause of syphilis), which appeared for the first time in Europe in 1495, came from older strains found in South America.

Two years later this triggers a terrible epidemic which spreads across Europe...

... thanks to the Italian wars. The Italians call it "the French disease", the French "the Neapolitan disease".

IT'S YOUR FAULT!

NO! IT'S YOUR FAULT!

Which in 1565 allows the Italian anatomist, Gabriele Fallopio — he of the tubes — to invent the modern condom, "Venus's glove", a simple linen sheath soaked in a solution of mercury.

AS FOR THE SIZE, IT'S BASED ON MY ANATOMY.

It's possible, however, that Fallopio's invention may have been a kind of dressing to heal syphilitic cankers rather than a genuine condom.

WELL?

I FEEL BETTER ALREADY!

Despite being banned by the Church for "obstructing providence", the condom had its hour of glory in the form of sheep-gut in the 18th century.

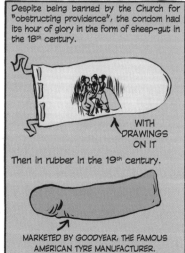

WITH DRAWINGS ON IT

Then in rubber in the 19th century.

MARKETED BY GOODYEAR, THE FAMOUS AMERICAN TYRE MANUFACTURER.

IMPOTENCE TRIBUNALS

Decided by families, arranged marriages rarely prove satisfying, but everyone has to make the best of it. To break off unwanted marriages it is therefore necessary to resort to subterfuge.

As the goal of marriage was procreation, wives and their families hit on grounds for annulment: the husband's impotence.

AHA! A CASE FOR ANNULMENT!

I'M JUST RELAXING...

And so impotence tribunals are established in the 16th century which will prevail until the 18th century — sexual impotence meaning the inability to carry out one's conjugal duties.

WOULD THE ACCUSED PLEASE RISE!

Upon receiving the wife's complaint, a preliminary inspection of the accused's member is carried out:

LAUGHABLE PENIS... NONDESCRIPT TESTICLES...

But more often than not the member is normal. The Congress is therefore called in: five matrons, five doctors and five surgeons. The man accused of impotence by his wife must comply by making love to her in front of this inquisitorial jury and fulfil the three requirements:

STAND!

ENTER!

SPRINKLE!

GOOD LUCK!

The man very rarely succeeds, so the verdict is delivered: he is impotent and the marriage is annulled!

GO ON, DO IT! GET IT UP!

This subterfuge worked so well that, for two centuries, the tribunals have an endless stream of unhappy wives delighted to have found a way of ridding themselves of an annoying husband.

NO HARD FEELINGS...

TART!

Poetic justice: the canonists discover female impotence and sometimes — though rarely! — a husband can make a complaint against his wife:

SHE'S SO NARROW I CAN'T GET IN.

They even invent the existence of a special membrane, the "velamen", an anatomical barrier closing the vagina and preventing the penis from entering!

I AM CERTAIN! SHE HAS A VELAMEN.

BUT HE'S NOT EVEN HARD!

THE HUMAN IMAGINATION HAS NO LIMITS!

REPRESSION

The end of the Renaissance brings with it a new wave of sexual repression.

In 1501 the Borgia Alexander VI's papal bull obliges printers to submit every book to the archbishopric for approval. This is the beginning of censorship.

CENSOR ALL OF THEM.

THIS ONE, ON THE OTHER HAND, I DON'T KNOW — IT'S NOT BAD...

IT'S THE BIBLE, YOUR EXCELLENCY.

In 1543 in Venice the first index is printed, a catalogue of books banned by the Vatican.

WHAT THE HELL IS THIS? IT'S BLOODY AWFUL! IT MUST BE BANNED!

IT'S THE INDEX, YOUR EXCELLENCY!

In 1599, a Spanish Jesuit, Father Tomás Sanchez, publishes his *Holy Sacrament of Matrimony*, a monumental work which describes, classifies, lists, discusses everything that is possible in carnal matters between men and women...

OH, I... I... I DISGUST MYSELF! I SICKEN MYSELF!

—URGH!

Making of it a veritable pornographic catalogue, but also a confessor's manual for centuries to come!

IF ANYONE NEEDS ME I'LL BE IN THE CONFESSIONAL WITH FATHER SANCHEZ'S CATALOGUE!

This man who, as is well known, died a virgin, asks, "is it legitimate to practice intromission elsewhere than in the appropriate vessel?" and denounces many sexual practices.

BUT FATHER...

YOU DON'T EVEN KNOW WHAT IT IS.

YES! YES! IT'S FOUL! IT'S GHASTLY!

The Renaissance has had its day. Once again, every advance in sexual freedom is swiftly followed by a wave of repression.

ONE STEP FORWARD...

THREE STEPS BACK.

CHAPTER 8

THE M WORD

An extraordinary story merits a chapter of its own, so clearly does it reflect how a first step towards sexual freedom is always followed by a repressive response from the Church and society. This is the story of the persecution of masturbation. The trouble begins in the 17th century with the discovery of reproductive cells, and causes great harm across Europe in the 18th and 19th centuries. More than the mere repression of sexual urges, this persecution is the response of a traditional society faced with the rise of individual autonomy — male and female — in pursuit of liberty.

We're at the start of the 17th century. Holland is admired for the quality of its optics — the reason why all the discoveries which follow in this period come from this part of Europe.

THEY'RE BEAUTIFUL, MY OPTICS!

THEY'RE BEAUTIFUL!

In 1604, in Amsterdam, Zacharias Janssen invents the microscope.

Sixty years later, in Delft, De Graaf discovers the ovarian follicule, and the female gamete.

OOOH!

It's the beginning of the theory of ovism: that a child is born of the female ovule alone.

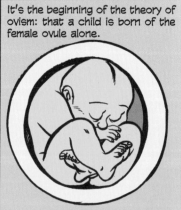

The woman, and the woman alone, is thus the womb of humanity. In a Europe still very much dominated by men, this theory encounters strong opposition.

AS FOR ME, I LIKE THIS THEORY!

ME TOO.

Fortunately, 15 years later — in Holland once again — Leeuwenhoek discovers the spermatozoid.

Curiously, Leeuwenhoek is a shopkeeper — a draper; passionate about optics, he uses microscopes to check the quality of his fabrics.

WOW!

RIGHT! IS HE REALLY GOING TO EXAMINE THEM ALL LIKE THAT?

His great curiosity leads him to become a biologist. With a microscope of his own making, he studies minute forms of life, discovers bacteria and micro-organisms.

WOW!

No one believes him.

YOU CAN'T SEE ANYTHING IN THIS, OLD BOY!

THAT SAID, I LOVE THE FABRIC OF YOUR SMOCK!

And one day, doubtless after masturbating...

AAAAH!

OH, DAMN IT! I'VE GOT IT ALL OVER THE MICROSCOPE!

... he observes with astonishment these kinds of tadpoles he calls "animalcules".

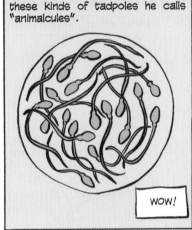

WOW!

What most amazes him is their number: "Sometimes there are over a thousand in a space the size of a grain of sand."

AND ALL THIS LITTLE WORLD COMES FROM ME?!

SO PROUD!

We are in the Europe of the naturalists — the biologists of the age — who are beginning to ponder sexuality. In 1675, Nicolas Venette's *Treaty on Conjugal Love* is published — in Amsterdam once again, a liberal town. This French physician tackles all questions about love and about relations between men and women, and makes no attempt to ban masturbation. For him freedom in relation to sexual urges is the sign of a healthy sex life. Though published under a pseudonym, this — the first genuine work of sexology — will be banned in France.

The discovery of the spermatozoid excites the great minds of the age: for those upholding the masculine order, the role of the man is recognized at last!

SO NOW BLOKES ARE GOING TO BE EVEN FURTHER UP THEIR OWN ARSES THAN BEFORE. GREAT — THANKS A BUNCH.

TWAT!

It's the start of the great battle between the ovists and the spermists — the former convinced the foetus is already wholly contained within the ovule, the latter convinced it is within the spermatozoids.

But the spermatozoid wins the day. Under the eye of the microscope, the scientists exclaim:

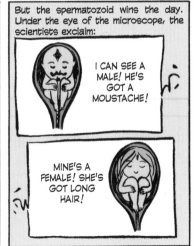

I CAN SEE A MALE! HE'S GOT A MOUSTACHE!

MINE'S A FEMALE! SHE'S GOT LONG HAIR!

113

News spreads very quickly, and the naturalists learn how to study the infinitesimal and to understand the existence of this spermatic animal:

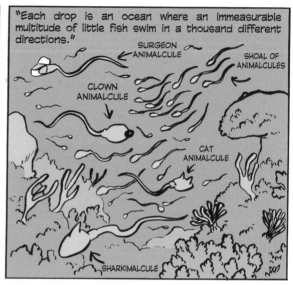

THESE ANIMALS HAVE A TAIL AND THEIR FORM IS RATHER LIKE THAT OF A FROG.

"Each drop is an ocean where an immeasurable multitude of little fish swim in a thousand different directions."

SURGEON ANIMALCULE

SHOAL OF ANIMALCULES

CLOWN ANIMALCULE

CAT ANIMALCULE

SHARKIMALCULE

BUT THEN COME SOME VERY SERIOUS QUESTIONS:

WHAT ARE THESE ANIMALS?

WHERE DO THEY COME FROM?

HAVE THEY BEEN AROUND SINCE CREATION

ARE THEY IMMORTAL

Hartsoecker tallies 300 million in a single drop of sperm.

CERTAINLY AS MANY AS THERE ARE HUMANS ON EARTH.

A flood of apocalyptic declarations follows: and what if Adam's testicles contained all the men to come?

THE FUTURE OF THE WORLD IS BETWEEN MY LEGS!

OR BETWEEN MINE!

And each man alive today, all the human beings to come?

YOU KNOW THAT WHEN YOU WHACK ME IN THE BALLS YOU'RE PUTTING THE WHOLE OF HUMANITY IN DANGER?

These scientists are perplexed but prudent — they ask questions but do not condemn anything. The ramifications of these questions will be left for the following century.

"If this is the case, the loss of sperm would signify the annihilation of humanity, the end of the world, the apocalypse."

"And ejaculation would be a suicidal act!"

A WET DREAM?!

WHAT HAVE YOU DONE, YOU WRETCH?

PERSECUTION

The first talk of a ban on masturbation occurs right at the start of the 18th century in Northern Europe. Under the influence of a Lutheran preacher, who goes on to teach in England, it is at first a protestant ban.

The apocalyptic message passes from the naturalists to the reformists, who are particularly strict when it comes to sexual morality.

HEY, GUYS! WE'VE FOUND A WAY TO STOP PEOPLE FROM MASTURBATING!

HOORAY!

AND IT'S SCIENTIFIC!

HOORAY!

The news thus travels from Holland to England then to Calvinist Switzerland. The strict eye of the Reformation takes a close look at solitary sex.

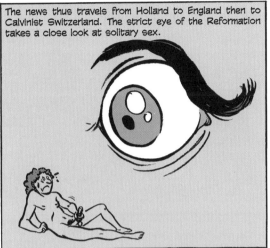

In London, in 1710, a charlatan claiming to be a physician — Doctor Bekkers — publishes a little brochure, *Onania*, which condemns "self-pollution".

IT'S AN ABOMINABLE SIN THAT LEADS TO CERTAIN DEATH!

IS THAT A "LITTLE DEATH"?

ONA BY Dr BE

His book is a great success for — a smart piece of marketing — it comes with an anti-masturbation powder costing 12 shillings a bottle, a cure for sex!

AND HERE'S YOUR POWDER TO NOT DIE.

A PHILANTHROPIST!

To grab people's attention and make his charlatan words more convincing, Bekkers looks to the Bible. As masturbation isn't mentioned, he finds something blameworthy that comes close to it: the crime of Onan — which thus, wrongly, leads to "onanism" being used to mean masturbation.

IT'S EVEN IN THE BIBLE — OH, YES!

12 SHILLINGS A BOTTLE.

In the Bible, Judah, founder of one of the seven tribes of Israel, has two sons: Er and Onan.

ER

ONAN

Er, the older of the two, dies.

TAMAR, ER'S WIFE

According to Levirate law, Onan, the younger brother, has to couple with his sister-in-law, Er's wife.

> MY BROTHER OR ME — WHAT'S THE DIFFERENCE?

But according to this law, the children of this union would be Er's.

> WHAT?!

> YOU WERE RIGHT: YOUR BROTHER OR YOU — WHAT'S THE DIFFERENCE?

Onan, not wanting such a child to be his brother's, withdraws before ejaculating and spills his seed.

> YOU MADE A MESS ON THE SHEETS!

Which angers God, who kills him.

> YOU MADE A MESS ON THE SHEETS!

So the crime of Onan was not masturbation but coitus interruptus — a method of contraception he therefore invented!

By naming masturbation "onanism", it becomes easy to claim a biblical prohibition, and to use this to control adolescent sexual urges. This is the beginning of two centuries of persecution for the most normal sexual practice — and the one most conducive to sexual fulfilment.

Next the great doctor Tissot of Lausanne picks up where Bekkers left off. Known throughout Europe for his treatment of smallpox, in 1758 Tissot publishes his *Essay on the Diseases Produced by Masturbation*, a genuine bestseller which was still being reprinted at the start of the 20th century.

> NOW IF THIS ONE DOESN'T FLY OFF THE SHELVES...!

It tells of the dreadful ravages caused by this shameful practice: "L.D. was a watchmaker who had enjoyed good health until the age of 17, at which age he began to masturbate — a vice he would indulge up to three times a day!"

> L.D.! WHAT ARE YOU DOING!

> ERR...I... I'M WINDING UP A CLOCK!

Tissot, horrified, pays him a visit. He finds a young boy, very weak and unable to make the slightest movement: "I found not so much a living being but a lifeless cadaver — penniless, pale, and emaciated... His soul, utterly abandoned to these vile habits, could hold no other ideas.

> WANKWANKWANK...

But the disease was too far advanced and he died a few weeks later."

✝
R.I.P.
L.D.
DEAD FROM TOO MUCH WANKING

This apocalyptic picture will serve over the centuries to petrify adolescents and deprive them of the natural form of sexual initiation.

> WITH THE TISSOT METHOD, I SAY "NO!" TO MASTURBATION!

REPRESSIVE VIOLENCE AND SADISTIC REMEDIES

In all four corners of Europe, the persecutors are stirring.

At first these are priests — Calvinist protestants — then the Catholic church gets involved, then physicians, moralists, and hygienists, who all weigh in with theories of their own...

"It's a sinful practice, a very recent perversion — it didn't exist in antiquity!"

"The inhabitants of the North are less inclined to this odious practice than those of the South. The warmer climate encourages this sin of lechery."

Insults fly — there are no words strong enough to condemn this plague. Priests, physicians, bishops, the pope... all castigate the teenager.

"It's a fatal advantage... a dangerous supplement!" declares the hypocritical Jean-Jacques Rousseau — himself an inveterate masturbator!

"We also have to be watchful for perversion among girls," the confessors warn, "for the size of the clitoris, which equals — and in some cases, exceeds — that of the penis, leads girls to abuse themselves with others."

The myth of the phallic woman — a woman who wants to make herself equal to men — comes to the fore! The clitoris, by this ploy, thus eclipses even the male organ in size!

This criminal clitoris must now be cut, burnt, castrated!

Female self-sufficiency implies an independence which is not to men's tastes.

THERE ARE WOMEN WHO HAVE SWORN TO ME THAT THEY HAVE FELT AN UNBEARABLE ITCH SINCE THE AGE OF 6.

LITTLE TARTS!

"So they rub away and use various objects: vegetables, tallow and wax candles, crystal stoppers, corks..."

SOOOOO... WHO AM I SLEEPING WITH TONIGHT?

Even more insufferable is the crime of the imagination — condemned along with masturbation.

Erotic fantasy offers an escape from the virtuous reality of a chaste sexuality.

A greater crime still: "To dare to think about sex in church and even to engage in it!"

HOW ABOUT IMAGINING THINKING ABOUT SEX IN CHURCH — IS THAT OKAY?

NO, YOU PERVERT!

Sex, down to the smallest details, becomes a reprehensible act. And having invented a disease, a remedy must now be found. These are many over the next few centuries — ingenious, malicious, sadistic, perverted...

The first of these is the act of confession to this abominable crime. Like a perverted voyeur, the priest questions, persists, wants to know everything and to obtain a confession.

YES... IT'S TRUE... I CONFESS...

AND HOW OFTEN DID THIS HAPPEN?

THREE TIMES A WEEK.

AND WHAT WERE YOU WEARING?

Then come potions, medicines, camphor, lilies — which would be strewn on the bed to preserve virtue. Next leeches are applied to the genitals... to mollify the penis.

FOR ONCE I'M GETTING OFF LIGHTLY...

In the 19th century, the age of technology, Doctor Lafond invents an anti-onanism corset which sells very well. It's a kind of strapping that prevents any kind of touching.

THERE'S NOT MUCH RISK OF US JUMPING ON EACH OTHER ANYWAY.

In the evening, teenagers' genitals are locked away in a case to keep them away from temptation.

GOOD NIGHT!

An English physician, Doctor Milton, invents a chastity belt which is kept firmly locked during the day, and a penis ring with raised spikes for the night.

FOR DAYTIME...

AND FOR NIGHTTIME

At the end of the 19th century, Doctor Demaux lodges a patent for a contraption designed for school dormitories: the head and the arms are kept away from the lower body by a sturdy wooden partition — an effective way to prevent any illicit acts.

SLEEP TIGHT!

Finally, if all these means prove insufficient, electrotherapy and surgery achieve marvellous results.

ISN'T PROGRESS WONDERFUL?

At the start of the 20th century, Doctor Lallemand warns, "Masturbation eats away at the social fabric, loosens the conjugal bond, and attacks the family — the very foundations of society..."

WILL WE COMPROMISE PROGRESS? WILL WE ALLOW MACHINES TO RUST WITH EJACULATE?

IN 1910 Freud himself and the first psychoanalysts wonder whether masturbation may be harmless, but struggle to find any answers.

IT'S A PRIMITIVE NEED.

Even today masturbation is still considered by psychoanalysis to be an infantile act.

"It's the pure demonic act!" says Jean-Paul Sartre — an enthusiast of self-love.

Despite the considerable progress made by feminism and later by sexual liberation, masturbation remained forbidden, reprehensible, discouraged until 1950; within religious institutions, it would endure long after this date as the *bête noire* of a regressive Church.

A SENSUAL TOUCH

Fortunately, from the start of this history, other voices have made themselves heard.

Firstly, Diderot speaks cautiously of a "sweet thing" ...

... of a "delicious moment".

As do the other great libertines of the 18th century, and notably the Marquis de Sade, who was a great enthusiast given he spent 27 years in prison.

AT LEAST I CAN WANK OVER MY WORKS!

But it's essentially in the second half of the 20th century that modern sexology will show all the benefits. Masturbation is at the heart of erotic creation — it allows for sexual maturation and maintains desire throughout adult life.

It is indispensable to women as it is to men. It was doubtless an anticipatory sense of its importance that led to masturbation being persecuted to the extent it was.

SO GO FORTH AND MASTURBATE!

CHAPTER 9

THE ENLIGHTENMENT: REPRESSION AND LIBERTINAGE

The Age of Enlightenment sees the real beginning of modernity in Europe, and is marked by an explosion in knowledge and a new spirit of critical inquiry.

Montesquieu, Voltaire, Rousseau, Hume, Goethe and Condorcet rethink the world,

Diderot and d'Alembert write the *Encyclopédie*.

Isaac Newton and Benjamin Franklin revolutionize physics; Bach and Mozart do the same for music.

Philosophers, writers, scientists, artists... lay the foundations for free thinking that distances itself from the prohibitions of the Ancien Régime. Royalty and religion are criticized, new ideas take their place. The century closes with the French Revolution.

The revolution is also one of social customs, it captivates men and women, and upsets the established order. The early days of marriages of love are poorly handled by the Church, which tries to reassert its authority over the family. The Enlightenment is an age of contrasts which sees both advances in freedom and a new wave of sexual repression (relative to masturbation, to homosexuality). The libertines, on the other hand, have a whale of a time...

WEDDINGS OF THE PEOPLE

The marriage of love struggles to find its place at the heart of the family. Among the peasantry, which constitutes 80% of the French population at the time, the spouse's choice timidly attempts to impose itself. The freedom of choice in love is obviously at its greatest when the family assets don't amount to much.

Meetings are quite ritualized, whether they take place while working in the fields, at Mass, at village fairs or festivals, on a Sunday evening...

OY! YOU KIDS! WE SAID WAIT 'TIL SUNDAY, NOT AT THE WAKE ON SUNDAY.

COO! COO! COO! COO!

If you're a boy, how do you tell a girl you fancy her? In the Gers region, you pinch her arm...

In the Béarn, you throw little pebbles at her...

In the Vendée, girls seem more enterprising:

PUT YOUR 'AND IN MINE AND GIMMEE A KEESS!

The boys reply:

PUT YOUR TONGUE DOWN MY GULLET AND ZAY YOU LERRVE ME!

But a teenage promise needs the family's say-so. You don't give your son or daughter away to just anyone! You find out more, make some inquiries, and use a "matchmaker" to take care of it.

SO IF YOU COULD FIND ANOTHER SWEETHEART FOR MY BOY — HE WANTS TO MARRY THAT UGLY COW, SUZON...

THAT'S MY DAUGHTER!

From now on the law demands parental consent before a marriage can be celebrated.

LIKE THAT WASN'T THE CASE BEFORE...

YES, BUT NOW IT'S WRITTEN IN LAW! SO NERR!

LA LOI

Saw and Noé met last summer at harvest time. Saw Bosquet is a saddler's daughter, and Noé Bourgeois the son of a foreman at the farm of Esclaponville.

They took a shine to each other, declared their love and the parents gave their approval.

The wedding will take place that winter, for no one ever gets married in summer as there's too much work to be done in the fields.

The bride is in red (always colourful), a white apron over her blouse. She takes her father's arm at the head of the procession to the church.

The wedding feast goes on into the night while the new couple take their leave.

A virgin, and terrified, the young bride must face the onslaught of an often brutal husband, as he brags about his previous experience with a servant or prostitute.

CHILL — IT'LL BE FINE... I ALMOST DID IT ONCE.

At the crack of dawn, a delegation barges into the bedroom to inspect the sheets...

SO THEN, KIDS! HAVE YOU MADE A RIGHT MESS OF THE SHEETS?

... then hang them out the window to show the neighbours — proof of the bride's virginity and thus of the husband's vigour.

THEY MADE A RIGHT MESS OF THE SHEETS!

HOORAY!

Saw and Noé are happy to be recognized as husband and wife.

TYING THE RIBBON

In this period it was vital for a man to prove his virility, for someone "tying the ribbon" on the big day could screw up the most idyllic of weddings.

Noé is quite worried — he fears the vengeance of a woman he spurned.

WHAT WAS I THINKING? NEARLY BANGING THE MAID OF HONOUR...

The tying of the ribbon is a magical spell which is typically cast at the church at the very moment of the benediction.

The sorcerer — or, typically, the sorceress — ties a thick ribbon around the penis of a young wolf (easy to find)...

A TRIPLE KNOT...

THAT'LL TEACH HIM A LESSON!

... then calls out to the victim.

NOÉ!

If he turns round, the die is cast and the man becomes impotent.

OH, NOT HER! SHE'S TIED THE RIBBON ON ME!

HAHAHA!

OOH! OOH!

OOH!

One can well imagine the terror these men must have felt when they became the despised target of a woman they dreaded.

There aren't any cures for the tying of the ribbon, other than some magic rituals, or prayers to Saint Vit, who had a reputation for helping men with sexual problems.

SAINT VIT — MAKE ME HARD!

Fortunately, Noé had a talisman on him, a very powerful love philter that stopped the sorceress in her tracks.

SO WHAT WAS IT THEN, THIS TALISMAN AGAINST THE SPELL?

I HAVEN'T A CLUE, DARLING, BUT I MUST HAVE HAD ONE OTHERWISE I WOULDN'T HAVE BEEN ABLE TO MAKE LOVE TO YOU.

THINK ABOUT IT.

The tying of the ribbon could thus be used as an excuse for unexplained sexual problems. This was the case of the unconsummated wedding night of Louis XVI (who was 16) and Marie-Antoinette (who was 14).

SOMEONE MUST HAVE TIED A RIBBON ON ME — IT'S THE ONLY RATIONAL EXPLANATION.

ACH, SCHEISSE...

In reality it was due to phimosis (tight foreskin) — only resolved by surgery seven years later!

MARRIAGE AND CHILDREN

After a wedding, family and friends generally expect a happy event within a year.

Religion is unequivocal: carnal relations only have one purpose — the child.

> RIGHT! THAT'S ENOUGH, NOW! STOP SCREWING AND START MAKING BABIES!

> CLAP CLAP

A childless couple is seen as cursed, humiliated.

> THEY AIN'T GOT NO CHILDREN! THEY AIN'T GOT NO CHILDREN!

> SAME TO YOU!

It is important to have several offspring to compensate for the very high rates of child mortality. And maternal mortality. Because the conditions for women are awful — one woman in six dies in childbirth.

> SO, SHALL WE TAKE BETS ON IT?

> 30 SOUS THAT ZOE SURVIVES!

> HAHA! YOU'RE ON!

God said to Eve she would give birth in pain: women are resigned to their fate. And if, during a difficult delivery, a choice between the mother and the child must be made, the Church recommends sacrificing the mother.

> NO WAY! DON'T EVEN THINK ABOUT IT! I'VE NOT SPENT 17 HOURS OF LABOUR TO SNUFF IT NOW!!!

> I KNOW, BUT THE BABY HASN'T HAD A CHANCE TO LIVE YET...

> SELFISH COW!

> This rule will still be in force at the start of the 20th century.

In the 18th century, because of the high mortality rates of men as well as women, marriages last no more than fifteen years, with one marriage in three being a remarriage.

> UNTIL DEATH DO YOU PART?

> I DON'T LIKE IT WHEN THEY SAY THAT.

> ME NEITHER.

And as all forms of contraceptive are forbidden by the Church, women on average bring 10 to 15 children into the world...

> OF COURSE WHEN YOU'VE SWORN A VOW OF CHASTITY...

> IT'S EASY!

... but few of them reach adulthood.

> AND HOW ARE THE TRIPLETS?

> TWINS. AS OF YESTERDAY.

> AND I'M WORRIED ONE OF THEM IS ABOUT TO BE AN ONLY CHILD.

> KOF KOF

Wars and epidemics also do their bit to shorten men's lives, but even more so those of women. It's better than the Middle Ages but still a long way from our own day.

> DON'T FEEL BAD FOR US! THINGS ARE GETTING MUCH BETTER ALL THE SAME!

PROMISCUITY AND CONTRACEPTION

Promiscuity is absolute in a century where people live together in very confined spaces — often in just a room or two.

In the bedrooms, and beds, men, women and children, brother and sisters, masters and servants, all pile in. This often gives rise to early erotic initiations, but also to abuse of all kinds. The sexual exploitation of servants is made easier by the "law" which allows the master to assert his rights of ownership.

Rape is the habitual lot of young women. But the authorities are clear: "It has been demonstrated that no adult woman can be raped against her will!" She is thus guilty of her own rape!

ERR... MASTER! EXCUSE ME BUT YOUR ARM'S DIGGING IN A LITTLE ...

IT'S NOT MY ARM.

LOUISON — I'M GOING TO RAPE YOU, IF THAT'S ALL RIGHT?

WELL, AS LONG AS IT'S CONSENSUAL RAPE...

In these conditions, the sexual intimacy of young married couples is virtually impossible.

Sexual pleasure becomes shameful. It's banned, and a "marital nightdress" invented with a single hole for procreation — so the husband is no longer exposed to his wife's nudity.

HEY, COME AND LOOK! OUR BRUV'S SCREWING HIS LADY WIFE OVER THERE!

YOU'RE WEARING LINGERIE?!!

YOU MINX!

The Church persecutes pleasure and guilty practices (masturbation). These become the "deadly secrets" of the confessional. Abortion, a mortal sin, leads to damnation and hell. In the 16th century, a woman convicted of abortion would be sentenced to death for murder; in the 18th century, she would face prison.

Although it is forbidden, abortion is nonetheless widespread, with dramatic consequences: a "child is sunk" either with a needle or with sprigs of parsley, with the wife the first to suffer.

Towards the end of the century, customs change — the "refusal of children" becomes widespread, coitus interruptus becomes a common contraceptive practice, and births are more spaced out.

HELP... HELP... THERE YOU GO!

THERE YOU GO!

THAT'S WHAT HAPPENS WHEN YOU MUCK ABOUT WITH SOME NEEDLES — YOU DO YOURSELF AN INJURY!

YOU'VE MADE A MESS ON THE SHEETS!

THAT'S ONE LESS MOUTH TO FEED!

HIGH SOCIETY

The age of Enlightenment is also one of great libertinage, particularly at the court of Louis XV.

Among the bourgeoisie and the minor nobility, marriage is always a family affair. It's the father who chooses his sons- and daughters-in-law, without considering the feelings of his own children. It's not about love — marriage is far too serious for that.

> FATHER, IS IT TRUE YOU WANT ME TO BE MARRIED TO MADEMOISELLE SUCHANDSUCH?

> SON, MIND YOUR OWN BUSINESS.

But among the grand aristocracy, different rules apply. At the court of Louis XV, *galanterie* reigns. Literary salons sharpen wits; writers and philosophers argue...

Watteau paints his *fêtes galantes*...

... and François Boucher his dazzling nudes.

In a climate of high courtliness, the nobility mingles with the dancers of the *Opéra* and the actresses of the *Comédie-Française* — ladies of very easy virtue. They meet in the Grande Galerie, surrender themselves in the gardens, romp in the hunting lodges...

The immediate consequence: syphilis reigns supreme and passes from sex to sex. Saint-Simon explains:

In almost 500 years, from the 16th to the 20th century, there were so many victims of syphilis that these have now been forgotten — even though all the good and the great of the world were affected.

What do Francis I, Henry VIII, Louis XIV, and Napoleon have in common?

> SYPHILIS!

"M. le Duc gave the pox to Mme de Prie.

Mme de Prie gave it to M. de Livry.

M. de Livry gave it to his wife.

His wife gave it to La Peyronie...

And La Peyronie, good doctor that he is, cured all of them!"

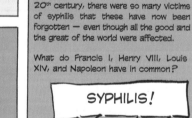

We are now in 1755: Louis XV is 45 years old, a good father, an affectionate if not very faithful husband.

DADDY PROMISED TO PLAY WITH US AFTER TAKING CARE OF THE NANNY.

YEESSS! OOOOH! YEESSS!

The king is known to have more than 60 concubines, including 16 favourites — the official mistresses — who live in Versailles.

MAJESTY! CLUCK
CLUCK YOOHOO!
CLUCK CLUCK
MAJESTY! CLUCK
YOOHOO! COOEEY!
YOUR HIGHNESS! CLUCK

But Madame de Pompadour establishes herself very quickly, determined to be the only one.

Born Jeanne Antoinette Poisson in Paris in 1721 into the petty bourgeoisie, when she is 9 a clairvoyant predicts:

YOU WILL BE THE KING'S MISTRESS.

WOW...

True enough, when Jeanne Antoinette is 24, and already married, Louis moves her to Versailles, into an apartment just above his own which he enters by a secret staircase.

MY CHILDHOOD DREAM HAS COME TRUE!

For five years she will be his sole mistress. She will thereafter remain his great favourite, and always be in charge of the king's pleasures.

Louis meets his other mistresses, prostitutes and libertine ladies in his "stag park", also known as the King's Birdcage, where Madame de Pompadour organizes extravagant feasts and masked balls...

... where the girls are ever younger...

EW, TAKE A BOUCHER'S AT MISS O'MURPHY – SHE LOOKS OLD ENOUGH TO BE MY WIFE!

Louis XV is without doubt the most sex-obsessed of all the kings of France.

THE DAFFODIL AND THE BIDET

The age of Enlightenment marks the turn towards modernity.

At the time, Versailles is a sumptuous château, a royal residence that is the envy of all Europe...

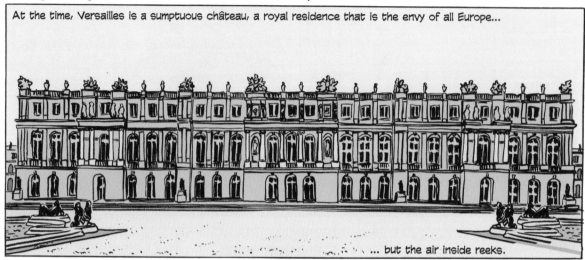

... but the air inside reeks.

No latrines, no privies. The passages, the courtyards, the corridors are all filled with urine and faeces.

Everyone pisses and shits on the spot! The stagnant water of the canals adds a final flourish to this terrible stench.

And it's in this very place that perfumes will blossom. All the court uses scent, wearing sachets of lavender, daffodil, perfumed gloves, and fragrant fans.

As Alain Corbin famously said, the miasma gives way to the daffodil.

BEFORE, IT SMELLED OF SHIT...

NOW, IT SMELLS OF SHIT AND DAFFODILS!

And with perfume comes love.

The bidet is invented in the same period.

NEW

Raised on four legs, the bidet shows how personal hygiene is improving, and how important the sexual act has become for a nobility that is already distinguishing between pleasure and procreation.

Mme de Pompadour's bidet is made of finely sculpted beech, lined with tin plate, and has a small lock. It's a sophisticated item for this temple of sensual love.

SO CLASSY!

"Galanterie" is the by-word for this world of courtesans, or high-class prostitutes.

IT GOES WITHOUT SAYING YOU'RE WELCOME TO USE THE BIDET...

And these ladies demand high prices, ruining the men who visit them: "For one night of love, Count Potocki sacrificed 12 000 livres, a house, and a lacquered coach!"

ALL THIS MUST HAVE COST YOU A FORTUNE!

ONLY A SMALL ONE — A NIGHT WITH POTOCKI!

Women strip seductively. The paintings of Boucher and Fragonard freely show female bodies — with buttocks triumphing over breasts!

In the Hôtel de la Chaussée-d'Antin a ballet called *Le Paradis terrestre* is performed — with the cast from the Opéra performing stark naked!

At the court, women are becoming emancipated, showing their bodies without much modesty.

The bust is squeezed into a corset with a plunging neckline to show off the whiteness of their skin, and velvet beauty spots add a finishing touch.

Postillons d'amour — small bejewelled necklaces — are draped over their half-bared breasts.

And beneath their crinoline skirts, which accentuate their narrow waists, layer upon layer of petticoats studded with pearls conceal stockings threaded with gold.

But never any knickers!

Only old ladies wear those, to hide parts that are longer of much use.

HMM, WELL NOT ALL OF THEM WEAR KNICKERS...

ART, SEX AND LITERATURE

This is still the age of salons, at which poets, writers and philosophers discuss love. And in these aristocratic circles, wealth, privilege, *galanterie* and libertinage all come together.

Sex and literature are hand in glove.

ESPECIALLY WHEN YOU'RE BORED IN BED!

ER... I DON'T THINK THAT'S WHAT THEY MEANT...

It's the great age of libertine, erotic and pornographic novels: Diderot's *Indiscreet Jewels*, Sade's *Justine*, the *Rutting Venus*...

Anticlerical novels in which priests exploit the confessional to seduce their parishioners.

All these books are put on the index of course, but they still circulate "under the coat"!

In this age of Enlightenment, important figures — notorious libertines — pass into posterity: Casanova, an inveterate seducer; Donatien, Marquis de Sade, sexual pervert; the Chevalier d'Éon, transvestite spy.

Giacomo Casanova is born in Venice, on the Calle de la Comedia, a name which suits him well. He is above all an adventurer who seduces and takes his pleasure without the slightest decorum.

He talks openly of his amorous adventures in his *Memoirs*, where he catalogues 142 conquests across Europe, from Venice to Paris, London to Moscow...

"I have loved woman madly, but I have always loved freedom more." So time after time he breaks with the former in search of new and boundless horizons.

HE DUMPED ME FOR LIBERTY!

HE WHAT? WHO'S SHE?

This worldly libertine, who is not handsome but sharp, witty and a great seducer, has been chasing petticoats since he was a child. By the age of 15, one of the servants in his house has already become his mistress.

WELL, WELL. WE DO LIKE BATHTIME, DON'T WE, MY LITTLE GIACOMO!

Destined for an ecclesiastical career, he becomes an Abbé...

AND OF COURSE, YOU'LL TAKE A VOW OF CHASTITY.

WHAT?!

...but very soon he has to give this up when word gets out he has run off with his French teacher's daughter.

Returning to Venice, he shares the favours of a nun with Abbé Bernis, a notorious libertine and future cardinal, in a bachelor pad where one of them watches behind a screen while the other is screwing away.

But going against the prevailing trend for condoms among libertines wary of the pox, Casanova adopts a haughty attitude:

I SHALL NEVER DECK MYSELF OUT IN SOME DEAD SKIN JUST TO PROVE I AM ALIVE!

YOU'RE RIGHT! LET'S SHARE OUR STDS!

His exploits are many, from barely pubescent servants to his own daughter, with whom he will have a child. The Inquisition weighs in, and Casanova is incarcerated in Venice in the dreadful *Piombi* prison...

I SMELL BURNING!

IT'S SUMMER!

AARGH! AARGH! AARGH! AARGH!

... from which he manages to escape a year later.

EXCUSE MY, MY GOOD MAN! I WAS OUT FOR A STROLL AND I'VE MANAGED TO LOCK MYSELF IN! COULD YOU LET ME OUT?

BUT OF COURSE, SIGNORE!

He then tours the courts, salons and brothels of Europe.

AND THEN — ABRACADABRA — I ESCAPE THE *PIOMBI*!

In Paris, at the Hôtel du roule, a famous brothel, he has his way for 14 hours in a row with one of the girls, who calls herself Saint-Hilaire.

IT'LL TAKE A WEEK FOR MY VAGINA TO RECOVER!

One evening in Cologne, at the opera, he seduces the mayor's wife.

At the time Casanova is living among the rats in a chapel, only going out to meet her in the evening and follow her back to her bedroom.

Their trysts continue — she thinks only of him, and brings him food, books and candles.

HAVE YOU GOT EVERYTHING YOU NEED, MY DEAR?

One fine day, as he always does, Casanova disappears as elegantly as he had arrived.

READY? CAN I TURN AROUND NOW?

NOT YET!

Five years later, in London, Miss Pauline reads a wanted ad: "Gentleman seeks lodger to rent part of his house." Casanova finds this lodger attractive, and declares his love. She rejects him.

NO WAY!

He falls from his horse — she rushes to his bedside...

ARE YOU OKAY, MY DEAR?

AARGH... MY KNEE HURTS A LITTLE, AARRRGH...

She falls into his arms and, once again, he disappears.

YOU WANT TO SEE A MAGIC TRICK?

?

Five years later, in Spain, Casanova approaches Ignazia. She falls in love with him and, as usual...

NOW YOU SEE ME...

...her lover disappears as suddenly as he had arrived.

NOW YOU DON'T.

Casanova ends his days rather sadly at the age of 73, a librarian at the château of Dux in Bohemia. He devotes his last 13 years to writing. His name is forever associated with lack of fulfilment in love — with the sense of being forever unable to find a soulmate, and of always fleeing in search of a new conquest.

LIKE A GREAT MAGICIAN, I TRANSFORMED MY LIFE INTO A MASTERPIECE

Donatien Alphonse François, Marquis de Sade, "the divine Marquis", was heir to one of the noblest families of Provence.

At 16, he is a brave cavalier in the war against Prussia.

At 22, he marries Renée-Pélagie de Montreuil, who will later remain loyal to him throughout his years in prison...

BUT THE MOMENT YOU'RE OUT — I'M OFF.

I CAN'T SAY I BLAME YOU, DEAR.

... even though he has spent much of her fortune. For the young Marquis leads many lives at once, frequenting brothels and using several bachelor pads in Paris and in the country.

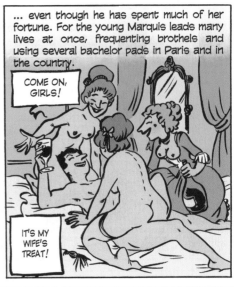

COME ON, GIRLS!

IT'S MY WIFE'S TREAT!

He is arrested the first time for "outrageous debauchery" and locked up in Vincennes after a prostitute complains about his sacrilegious practices and threatening behaviour.

WELL FINE, BUT WHEN YOU TELL ME "YOU CAN DO ANYTHING YOU WANT", WELL...

PERVERT!

Sade's crimes and scandals become the talk of France.

Another woman makes a complaint against him, claiming he tied her to a bed, burnt her, and flogged her. Sade's life is nothing but a succession of "sadistic" pleasures.

AAAAH!

WHOOPS!

With the king's indulgence he only spends six months in prison, and is ordered to return to his château in Provence — where he embarks on a passionate affair with Anne-Prospère, his young sister-in-law, a Benedictine canoness.

YOU REALLY WANT ME TO KEEP THE HABIT ON?

YOU BET!

When he is 32, he organizes an evening of great debauchery with several prostitutes, to whom he gives chocolate-coated Spanish Fly — the most powerful, and the most dangerous, of aphrodisiacs! The prostitutes think they have been poisoned.

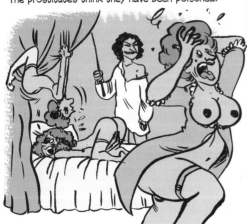

Sade is charged with poisoning and sodomy and condemned to death — but he's already escaped to Italy with Anne-Prospère, who declares her undying love for him.

I SWEAR TO M. LE MARQUIS DE SADE, MY LOVER, TO ALWAYS BE HIS AND HIS ALONE...

SIGN IT WITH YOUR BLOOD, NOW.

They make their way to Venice until, confronted with her lover's infidelities, she packs her bags and leaves.

WELL! THOSE PRETTY PROMISES DIDN'T LAST LONG!

In 1777, at the age of 36, he is arrested again and incarcerated first in the dungeon of Vincennes then the Bastille, which he will leave on 4 July 1789 — a few days before the Revolutionary insurrection — for the asylum in Charenton.

COULDN'T THEY HAVE STORMED THE BASTILLE 10 DAYS EARLIER?

Thirteen years of captivity during which, after a life of passion and adventure, he becomes a writer, organizing his ideas and putting them down on paper.

PHWOAARR!

YOU LITTLE MINXES!

Sade's imagination becomes an outlet for his perverted urges. He writes *Justine*, and *The 120 Days of Sodom*, in which he depicts the eroticism and sadistic violence still associated with his name today.

Charles de Beaumont, the Chevalier d'Éon, is born in 1728, the son of a lawyer at the Courts of Justice in Paris.

A lawyer himself, he is recruited by the "king's secret", Louis XVI's covert cabinet.

An ambassador at the Russian court, he appears there in the guise of a woman, Lia de Beaumont. He then takes part in military campaigns as a man, before leaving for London, where he insists he has always been a woman.

YES, I'M A WOMAN!

I JUST DIDN'T SHAVE THIS MORNING, THAT'S ALL.

He is called a madman, a hermaphrodite, a man or a woman! At the court of Louis XVI, where he appears as a woman of course, he serves as an object of curiosity for all of Paris.

THEY SAY HE HAS BREASTS!

THEY SAY SHE HAS BALLS!

He continues his escapades in London and Paris, as a woman still, using his talent at fencing to win several duels, and dies in penury at the age of 81.

At his death, it was confirmed that he was physically a man, but his determination to live as a woman led to the term "eonism" for transvestism. It is not impossible that he may have been an example of transsexualism, the profound conviction of having an identity different to one's anatomical sex.

THE FREEDOM OF THE DIRECTORY

In 1789, nudity hits the streets.

The "sans-culottes" expose the buttocks of pretty aristocrats to administer a patriotic smack. Obscenity replaces the refined eroticism of the Age of Enlightenment.

AARGH! A SANS-CULOTTE!

LOOK WHO'S TALKING!

Then, after three years of terror and public executions, the Directory ends the century with a flourish of extravagance. A new world seems to emerge with new horizons, new money and new morals. It's a time for going a little overboard — the age of the *Incroyables* and the *Merveilleuses* — a reaction against the horrors of the all too recent past.

In Paris, morals become more relaxed, parties and balls abound, along with prostitution...

For a while homosexuality shows its face a little more openly.

A few lady libertines dare to flaunt themselves with provocative exhibitionism. Mme Tallien, the most famous of the *Merveilleuses*, strolls defiantly down the Champs-Élysées with a friend — the two of them naked but for their see-through gossamer dresses. Others dare to show their bare breasts in public.

At the same time, Napoleon, during his campaign in Egypt, famously writes to Joséphine:

DON'T WASH! I'M COMING!

... Rightly sensing the aphrodisiac effect of natural scents...

Though it did take a fair old time to get back from Egypt!

WHEN YOU SAY "DON'T WASH!" — I DON'T WASH.

I DIDN'T THINK!

The Directory, this breath of fresh air, only lasts for four years, from 1795 to 1799. As ever, this greater freedom is followed by a period of repression. Under Bonaparte, the Consulate takes matters in hand with a social, political and moral clampdown.

THAT'S ENOUGH OF THAT CRAP!

CHAPTER 10

THE 19TH CENTURY: CLENCHED BUTTOCKS AND PROSTITUTION

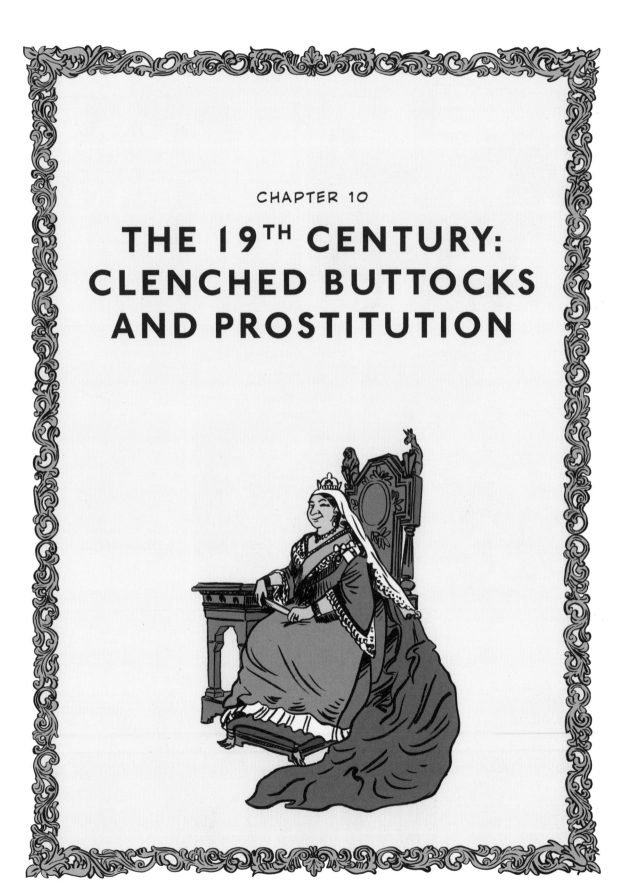

As the age of Enlightenment draws to a close, love and reproduction seem reconciled in marriage, but the rise of the bourgeoisie ushers in a new age of prudery.

OF COURSE WE'VE DONE IT BEFORE!

TWICE!

This 19th century is one of paradoxes: on the one hand prostitution is on the rise, on the other bourgeois puritanism is championing the chastity of the ideal woman.

...BUT FOR SOME...

WE MAY NOT BE THE INCARNATION OF PURITY...

... WE TOO CAN BE "IDEAL WOMEN"!

It is also the century of colonialism, with travellers bringing home exotic customs from the ends of the earth.

HOW SATISFYING IT IS TO BRING CULTURE AND CIVILIZATION TO THESE SAVAGES.

In France, Bonaparte takes power and becomes Napoleon I, Emperor of the French, in 1804.

THE LAW — THAT'S ME!

The Napoleonic Code is published the same year and guarantees the principles of freedom and equality, but reinforces social inequalities...

CODE NAPOLÉON

LADIES, YOU'RE GOING TO LOVE IT!

... asserting the superiority of the employer over the employee...

... the husband over his wife, and the father over his children.

Victorian England will go further still in delivering a message of austerity, decency and moral rigour.

EDWARD, YOU ARE NOW OLD ENOUGH TO HAVE YOUR FIRST BROOM UP YOUR ARSE.

JUST LIKE YOUR FATHER AND MOTHER.

—JOY!

THE HORNY EMPEROR

Napoleon lives life in the fast lane — both in his military career and in his love affairs. An officer at 16, a general at 25, a consul at 30, an emperor at 35, he will marry twice and have more than 50 mistresses!

In 1795, when he is 25, Napoleon is engaged to Désirée Clary when he falls in love with Joséphine de Beauharnais, whom he marries a year later.

Désirée will console herself by marrying Bernadotte, and will become queen of Sweden.

FUCK NAP'!

Napoleon is 27, Joséphine 33 — he is desperately in love...

THE CAMPAIGN IN ITALY IS GOING TO BE TORTURE WITHOUT YOU.

She fools around in the libertarian Paris of the Consulate, while he pursues his campaign in Italy.

WHOOPS... NAP'! WEREN'T YOU SUPPOSED TO BE BACK IN A MONTH OR SO?

SURPRISE.

As Joséphine could not give him children, Napoleon repudiates her. They separate in 1809 using the very divorce law he had enshrined in his civil Code.

THERE! I'VE SIGNED! YOU HAPPY?

GOOD RIDDANCE!

A year later he marries Marie Louise of Austria while he is still having an affair with Marie Walewska, with whom he will have a child that same year!

MARIE LOUISE — YOU'VE MADE ME SO HAPPY WITH OUR SON!

I'VE NOT EVEN GIVEN BIRTH YET...

Napoleon's life continues at a breakneck pace, with a new military or amorous conquest each year — and almost as many bastards — a sign either of the absence of contraception, or of the mistresses' desire to maintain their association with the emperor!

The Napoleonic epic concludes in Saint-Helena. At his death in 1821, legend has it that the emperor's penis is removed during the autopsy. A relic for some, a trophy for others — an emperor's member offers a posthumous symbol of power.

HYPOCRISY OR PRUDERY?

One empire falls, another rises. This age will bear the name of the queen who reigned 63 years over the immense British Empire, from Canada to Australia, and imposed that protestant severity known as prudery.

Victoria is only 18 when she ascends to the throne. Immediately, protestants from all over Europe flock to her.

I DON'T THINK THIS IS JUST ABOUT MY BIKINI BOD...

ME! ME! ME! ME! ME! ME! ME!

She falls in love with Albert of Saxony, with whom she will have nine children in only 15 years. For the Empire, Victoria and Albert represent a model couple, surrounded by their numerous offspring.

In the public imagination, Victoria is an austere queen...

IF WE ARE NOT AMUSED, NO ONE ELSE SHALL BE EITHER.

But in private, Victoria and Albert are very much in love, and very loving. Contrary to popular belief, the queen loves sex with a passion.

YOU MINX!

MOOORRE!

In their apartments, pride of place goes to a gift from the queen to her husband: a painting in which naked nymphs prepare to bathe while a prince secretly looks on.

OOOH... YOU MINX!

By the bed, and within reach, there is a lever that Albert pulls on to lock the door, preventing any interruption.

NO — LEAVE IT OPEN! IT TURNS ME ON...

YOU MINX!

OPEN

CLOSED

The genital piercing known as a "Prince Albert" is a ring inserted through the urethra in the glans of the penis.

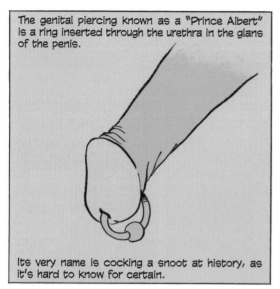

Its very name is cocking a snoot at history, as it's hard to know for certain.

Legend has it that Prince Albert was known for his sudden unwanted erections, which would protrude in the close-fitting trousers required for official receptions.

AWKWAAAARD!

YOUR HIGHNESS...

It seems that the idea for this piercing came from an English dandy, George "Beau" Brummel, who had a penis ring inserted so it could be tied against his thigh with a thin cord.

SO CHIC!

This kept his penis in place in case of erection...

SO SMART!

This erotic idiosyncrasy would no doubt have amused the queen.

STOP IT...

RIDE A COCK HORSE...

In 1861, when Albert died, Victoria was a young widow of 42, profoundly affected by the loss of her husband. She remained at the head of the Empire until her death in 1901.

BOOHOO... IT REMINDS ME SO MUCH OF YOUR GRANDFATHER...

?

If the word "puritanism" is still associated with her Empire and the age she lived in, this reflects the huge influence of the British Empire at this time. For this prudery existed long before Victoria's reign, the hallmark of "polite" British society, and its influence spreads to America too.

AFTER YOU, DEAR BOY.

NO, I INSIST — AFTER YOU.

I COULDN'T.

REALLY, I INSIST.

In England it's the age of sensitive souls, of women who cannot bear the slightest mention of sex. The names of animals branded by their sex, such as "bitch" or "stallion", disappear from use.

The word "leg" becomes dubious — forbidden for being too suggestive, and replaced by "limb" in relation to animals...

One does not say:

LOOK! A BITCH AND A STALLION SHAGGING!

One does say:

LOOK! A FEMALE CANINE AND A MALE MARE SHAGGING!

AND WHAT IF ONE WERE TO MENTION ELEPHANTS' ENORMOUS MEMBERS, FOR EXAMPLE?

OOOH! "ELEPHANT"?

SHOCKING!

... or even the feet of a piano, which are now covered in lace and a sheet to hide the nudity of these "legs" which might otherwise shock chaste young ladies.

PERSONALLY, I FIND ALL THIS LINGERIE VERY SAUCY!

To say the word "trousers", or to talk about the fertilization of flowers, was thus akin to pornography.

OH, MOTHER — LOOK! THERE ARE LOADS OF BEES ALL OVER THOSE FLOWERS!

MARY-ROSE! DO YOU MIND!

ANY MORE OF THAT FILTH AND YOU'LL GET A DAMN GOOD THRASHING!

In France, at this time, a dictionary of decorum advocates abolishing any syllables that are too evocative of sex: one would therefore no longer say "confiture" (jam), but "fiture" ("con" being a vulgar term for the vagina)!

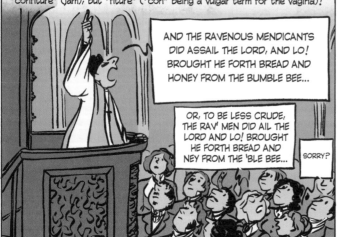

AND THE RAVENOUS MENDICANTS DID ASSAIL THE LORD, AND LO! BROUGHT HE FORTH BREAD AND HONEY FROM THE BUMBLE BEE...

OR, TO BE LESS CRUDE, THE RAV' MEN DID AIL THE LORD AND LO! BROUGHT HE FORTH BREAD AND NEY FROM THE 'BLE BEE...

SORRY?

In this empire of propriety, the plight of women is neglected: the ideal of a pure and innocent creature coincides with the stripping of civil rights for women. The married woman is a lesser being without rights — neither the right to vote nor the right to property. She possesses no assets of her own. Her role as mother, and mistress of the house, excludes the possibility of any employment other than teaching.

OH, I SEE...

SO, WOMAN = MISTRESS — END OF.

OOOH, "MISTRESS?"

SHOCKING!

THE CULT OF PURITY

In this age of paradoxes, with debauchery, loose morals, and prostitution on the rise, virginity seems to offer a bastion against depravity.

The pure virgin, innocent, ignorant of sin, is a source of grace, perfection, sweetness and discretion. She is the ideal woman.

AND IT GOES FOR ALL AGES!

Around 1850, the cult of Mary emerges and, a few years later in 1858, an apparition of the Virgin appears to Bernadette, telling her:

I AM THE IMMACULATE CONCEPTION.

Virginity thus fascinates the mystics. Everything must be done to preserve the purity of young girls. This is the start of weddings in white and orange blossoms, a symbol of virginity worn by the husband on the lapel.

RED WAS A LITTLE WHORISH.

Religious boarding houses keep watch over virginal purity, the clergy declares itself opposed to bathing (because of the nudity) and to dancing (an immoral practice, the cause of debauchery) — all this out of fear of the awakening of sexual desire.

ME, I'M NOT GOING TO BATHE ANYMORE.

THAT WAY NO ONE WILL INVITE ME TO THE BALL AND I'LL STAY PURE.

SUCH A MODEL OF VIRTUE, MY GIRL...

Sexual morality invites itself into the lives of couples with the conjugal duties imposed on husband and wife: the mastery of sexual urges...

NOAH, I WAS WONDERING IF, POSSIBLY...

A LITTLE SELF-CONTROL, MY DEAR. CALM YOURSELF.

... but above all not to rebuff a husband's advances!

I WANT YOU...

WHAT?! THIS IS REALLY NOT THE TIME!

NOW, NOW! CONJUGAL DUTY!

One doubt lingers: should a consenting woman deny herself an orgasm? According to several theologians:

YES!

But some begin to argue that orgasm should not be considered a sin.

YESSS!

All believers must nonetheless follow the advice of their spiritual advisor...

ONE POSITION ONLY: MISSIONARY! AND NO ORGASM!

CHEF YES CHEF!

... and to confess their offences against morality.

WE DID IT FROM BEHIND....

WHAT? LIKE DOGS! THAT WILL BE THREE OUR FATHERS!

CHEF YES CHEF!

The clergy don't like animals, especially doggies!

CHEF YES CHEF!

"Our greatest enemy is our own body", one implacably severe ecclesiastic will say.

It is also the start of new standards of sanitation and hygiene.

EEEEWW!

SO IT'S NOT BULLSHIT — WE REALLY DO NEED TO WASH!

Much is made of the perils of venereal disease, and syphilis in particular, which is wreaking havoc across the whole of Europe, affecting every class of society. Flaubert says that it is as rife as the common cold! The world of prostitution magnifies the problem dramatically.

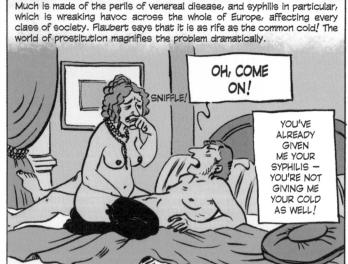

SNIFFLE!

OH, COME ON!

YOU'VE ALREADY GIVEN ME YOUR SYPHILIS — YOU'RE NOT GIVING ME YOUR COLD AS WELL!

During sanitary checks on brothels, the doctor, by using the same speculum, would pass on the infection to all the other prostitutes.

OH, IT'S FINE. NICE AND CLEAN!

RUB RUB

A sexually transmitted disease, syphilis affects between 15 and 20% of the population, causing thousands of deaths each year, and thousands of still-born babies. Because it attacks the brain, it is the leading cause of madness!

Baudelaire, Toulouse-Lautrec, Gauguin, Rimbaud... all afflicted with syphilis, with Nerval and Maupassant both suffering from syphilitic madness.

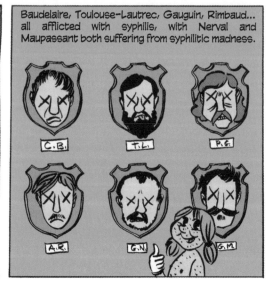

C.B.

T.L.

P.G.

A.R.

G.N.

G.M.

THE AGE OF BROTHELS

With the rise of the great cities, institutionalized prostitution becomes established across Europe.

The brothel becomes a place to meet and unwind, a part of men's social life.

In England there are over 5000 of them in an era when there are only 2150 churches, schools and institutions!

SO, BETWEEN SCREWING, PRAYING, LEARNING AND WORKING, MEN ENJOY SCREWING TWICE AS MUCH.

IT'S JUST MATHS.

SHOCKING!

In London, touts make a living from recruiting very young girls, as the age of consent is 12 years old.

WHAT'LL YOU GIVE ME FOR THE LITTLE 'UN?

SHE'S 12 MONTHS OLD!

In 1810, aside from the Palais-Royal district, where all pleasures can be had, there are no less than 180 official brothels in Paris.

Prostitution is considered at the time to be a "necessary evil". At the end of the 19th century, records suggest the number of prostitutes in Paris is 155 000 — and this does not include those working in clandestine brothels. The trafficking of these women reaches such a scale that there is talk of a "white slave trade". Abolitionists start to make their voices heard.

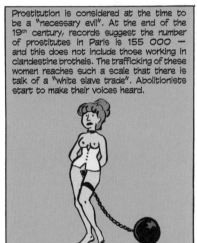

The Englishwoman Josephine Butler, a militant feminist, succeeds in uniting abolitionists all across Europe, haranguing the crowds at market squares, condemning the enslavement of women.

FREE THESE SEX SLAVES!

Bourgeois hypocrisy does the splits: the good family man preaches fidelity but screws the servants and visits brothels.

AND A GOOD HUSBAND MUST ALWAYS BE FAITHFUL TO HIS WIFE.

DON'T MAKE ME LAUGH...

Society has fortunately thought of everything: a law forbidding paternity tests stops maids from collecting their dues, and only wives can be punished for adultery.

CAN YOU EXPLAIN THIS, DEAR?

YOU'RE MISTAKEN, ALPHONSE. I'M NOT THE ONE WHO'S JUST GIVEN BIRTH. I WOULD HAVE TO HAVE BEEN PREGNANT FIRST.

ANYWAY THIS CHILD LOOKS JUST LIKE YOU...

EXOTICISM

Exoticism combines the innocence of nudity with foreign customs and moral freedom.

Thus, at the end of the 18th century, Bougainville had stirred French readers with his account of Tahiti, a "Garden of Eden", where everyone makes love freely and without inhibition.

HE WAS RIGHT! IT IS PARADISE — EVERYONE'S NAKED HERE!

In the 19th century, orientalism inflames the Western erotic imaginary. Istanbul is the stuff of dreams, with its abundance of women and steamy harems.

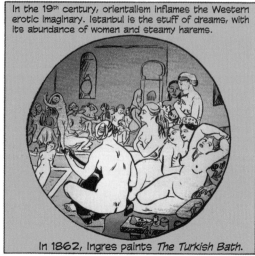

In 1862, Ingres paints *The Turkish Bath*.

In 1850, Flaubert travels to Egypt with Maxime du Camp. Sexual freedom, forbidden in Europe, seems within reach here.

THERE IS NOWHERE FINER THAN THE "WHORES' QUARTER"...

THEY CALL AFTER YOU...

Colonialism will be fuelled by these venal comforts. In 1883, the writer, diplomat and erotomaniac Richard Burton translates the *Kama Sutra*.

NEED TO FIND SOMETHING DEAD SEXY...

"THE OYSTER POSITION"!

As the *Obscene Publications Act* of 1857 bans the public circulation of such works, he creates the Kama Shastra Society to distribute it to his fellow members.

SNIGGER!

CORRR!

YOU CAN SEE HIS WILLY!

IT'S DEADLY SERIOUS, THIS SECRET SOCIETY...

And two years later, he will also circulate an unexpurgated version of the *Arabian Nights*.

ARABIAN NIGHTS X RATED

The *Kama Sutra*, considered scandalous at the time for its description of 64 sexual positions, will only be published legally in Britain in 1962!

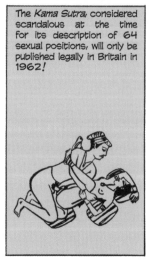

148

In 1857, Baudelaire causes an outcry in the press with his *Flowers of Evil*, poems deemed erotic and pornographic, condemned and censored as an offence against religious values and an outrage against public decency.

THIS GUY IS SICK.

THE P OF CH BAUDELA

HE'S A NUT

Manet exhibits his *Déjeuner sur l'herbe* (1863), the subject of which causes a shock: a naked woman sharing a picnic with fully clothed men...

IT'S BADLY PAINTED...

AND I DON'T LIKE IT.

THE PERSPECTIVE IS ALL WRONG...

Two years later, he exhibits *Olympia*, which prompts a national scandal. Zola is forced to defend it.

YELLOW-BELLIED ODALISQUE!

NO CLASS...

AND I DON'T LIKE IT.

Courbet's very famous painting, *L'Origine du monde*, painted in 1866, doesn't cause a scandal as it is never shown...

... except to a few friends of its successive owners — and even then, it remains hidden beneath another canvas depicting the Château de Blonay.

AND YOU KNOW WHAT? BEHIND IT THERE'S A FANNY...

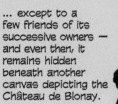

It is a hypocritical age of hidden sex, of one painting concealing another, of suggestive bronzes, libertine statues, and erotic scenes hidden on the back of a pocket watch, or in a case with a false bottom...

DAYLIGHT

BACKLIGHT

This is the age of the *Enfer* — or Hell — of the French National Library, the store room where all those works considered licentious, pornographic or placed on the index, are kept away from the public. Access was evidently only granted, with special approval, to men, then later to certain writers and researchers.

HELL

THAT'S NOT GOING TO BE POSSIBLE...

HUGO, SUPERMAN

Victor Hugo led a love life as giddily paced as his literary works.

At 17, Victor kisses Adèle for the first time. The Hugos and the Fouchers live in the same building. Victor and Adèle are childhood friends but Mme Hugo is against them marrying.

In 1821, when Victor is 19, his mother dies.

YES!

At last he can marry the love of his life. The wedding night is torrid!

I MADE LOVE TO HER NINE TIMES!

But Adèle finds it hard to cope with this force of nature — a writer and politician who lives, writes and loves in a frenzy.

After five pregnancies in six years she has had enough. She withdraws from a sexual life that does not suit her and begins an affair with Sainte-Beuve, the famous literary critic — a lover whose hermaphroditism makes him a morose lover.

YOU'LL BE BORED WITH ME — I HARDLY EVER MAKE LOVE.

REALLY? THAT'S PERFECT!

I COULDN'T ASK FOR MORE!

In 1833, Victor meets Juliette. He is 31, and she is 29. They will remain lovers for 50 years and will write more than 40 000 letters or *billets doux* — one of the largest collections of love letters.

WHAT ARE YOU DOING, MY LITTLE TOTO?

I'M WRITING TO YOU, MY LITTLE JUJU!

Later, his affair with Juliette loses its lustre, and with Adèle deserting him for Sainte-Beuve, Victor finds love again with young Léonie. She becomes his mistress, despite the 22-year age gap.

On 5 July 1845, at 6 o'clock in the morning, the police arrive and confirm an act of adultery. Léonie is imprisoned but Victor is in the clear.

SORRY.

But it takes more than this to put the brakes on Victor's insatiable ardour — endlessly fuelled by fresh conquests. He notes everything down in his secret notebooks. The old dog will have mistresses until his death, at 83 years old.

AND THAT'S A LOT OF WOMEN!

GEORGE, WONDERWOMAN

Aurore Dupin is born in 1804.

Her grandmother by marriage, Louise Dupin, was her heroine. She had hosted a literary salon in the Paris of the Enlightenment, rubbing shoulders with Voltaire, Marivaux, Montesquieu...

Married very young to Casimir Dudevant, Aurore learns about life at 24 with Aurélien, her first lover...

WOW! SO THAT'S WHAT SEX IS! COOOOL...

COOOOL...

... then with Stéphane, a childhood friend.

Aurore discovers the freedom of being a woman. She separates from her husband.

WHAT DO YOU MEAN BY A "LEGAL SEPARATION", MY DEAR?

WE WON'T SCREW ANYMORE, WE WON'T LIVE TOGETHER ANYMORE, BUT IN THE EYES OF GOD, WE'LL BE ABOVE BOARD.

During the revolutionary days of July 1830, with Paris chanting "Vive la liberté!", she meets Jules Sandeau. Both writers, they become lovers and lead a romantic, bohemian life together.

GET A ROOM!

DO YOU MIND? ARE WE SPOILING THE MOOD?

Aurore cuts her hair, obtains an official "permission to cross-dress", wears a man's suit ("less expensive", she says), takes the first name George and part of her lover's surname. George Sand is born. Taking up the defence of women, she fights against marriage — "a condition of eternal minority."

IT IS TIME TO RESTORE TO WOMEN THE CIVIL RIGHTS THAT MARRIAGE HAS TAKEN FROM THEM...

George Sand thrives on passion. She has numerous lovers before a blazing but tempestuous affair with Alfred de Musset.

When I lay at your feet an eternal homage,
Would you like me to wear a different visage?
You have captured the feelings of a heart
Formed by the Creator to kiss every part
Of you, my love, and my dreaming quill
Leaves thoughts on the page, unspoken still.
Of these lines read the first words with care
Then you will know the cure for my despair.

This signal favour you count without shame
Would vex my soul and lessen my fame.

She will then have an enduring affair with Chopin. She meets him when she is 32, and he 26. They will be lovers for 10 years, first in Majorca, then in Nohant, George's house.

OH! DO YOU KNOW RAVEL'S BOLERO?

George Sand spends the rest of her days in Nohant, the *grande dame* of popular fiction, defying social conventions and ushering in the liberation of women.

FOR ME, THE FREEDOM TO THINK AND ACT IS THE GREATEST OF GIFTS.

THE BEGINNINGS OF SEXOLOGY

Interest in the study of sexuality begins to grow.

In 1802 the great English physician, Thomas Beddoes, gives the first lesson in sexual education with a public demonstration of the differences between the sexes.

BOYS — THEY HAVE WILLIES.

AND GIRLS — THEY HAVE FANNIES.

OOOH!!!

OOOH! OOOH!!

Some physicians dare to talk about impotence and infertility.

YES, BUT THAT'S ONLY AMONG WOMEN, IS IT NOT?

ER, NO. WELL, IN FACT, ER...

A small revolution: in 1843, the great German biologist Bischoff reveals the spontaneous nature of ovulation.

SO THE FEMALE ORGASM IS NOT LINKED TO PROCREATION...

NOW THAT — THAT'S GOING TO CAUSE A STIR!

From now on, sexuality no longer depends on fertility. This is a giant step towards female emancipation...

HEY! FANCY A SHAG?

YOU WANT ANOTHER CHILD?

NO, I JUST WANT A SHAG!

... but a victory for the Church, which maintains that pleasure is not necessary to procreation.

YOU SURE YOU DIDN'T GET A KICK OUT OF MAKING THAT ONE?

THE VERY THOUGHT, FATHER!

PUT MY MIND AT REST...

OH, NOOO!

Twenty years later, the physiologist Eckart reveals the erection to be a reflex.

SORRY — I THOUGHT YOU HAD TO TAP IT LIKE YOU DO THE KNEE!

In literature, Stendhal becomes the theoretician of feelings. In 1825, he publishes his declaration of faith, *De l'amour*, in which he distinguishes between four different kinds of love: passionate love, tasteful love, physical love, and vain love. Only the first finds favour with him:

THIS IS WHAT HAPPENS IN THE SOUL ...

1 — First admiration.

WOW!

2 — One tells oneself "What a pleasure it would be to kiss her and be kissed by her."

SMACK! SMOOCH! MWAA! MWAA

3 — Next, hope: the eyes blush with emotion.

4 — All the signs of passion are now present: love is born.

This is Stendhal's famous "crystallization".

IT'S SIMPLE, ONE ONLY HAS TO THINK OF SOMETHING PFRFECT IN ORDER TO SEE IT IN THE ONE WE LOVE

Four years later, in his *Physiology of marriage*, Balzac denounces the religious and bourgeois hypocrisy of marriage. He has some very modern ideas...

THE FATE OF A COUPLE DEPENDS ON THE FIRST NIGHT.

NEVER BEGIN A MARRIAGE WITH RAPE.

OH, REALLY?

... but also some very misogynistic ones: "A woman never gossips more than when she keeps quiet".

NO NEED TO SAY A WORD...

YOUR BOREDOM SPEAKS VOLUMES.

The publication in 1886 of a medical textbook, Richard von Krafft-Ebing's *Psychopathia Sexualis*, marks a profound change in the understanding of sexuality and its troubles.

Sex, which had traditionally fallen within the purview of the law and the Church, now enters the field of psychiatry.

Fetishism...

...sadism...

...erotomania...

are no longer crimes but mental illnesses. This psychopathology textbook, with its Latin title, decriminalizes sexual crimes and simultaneously reduces them to the level of psychiatric disorders.

...homosexuality...

THE BIRTH OF HOMOSEXUALITY

Though considerable progress had been made under the Revolution with the decriminalization of homosexuality in 1791...

... homosexuals continue to be harassed and pursued by the police for "indecent exposure" throughout the 19th and 20th centuries.

I AM ARRESTING YOU FOR INDECENT EXPOSURE!

IN OUR OWN HOME?

THE BIG BOOK OF "POOFS" BY THE POLICE

PUT IT ON THE INDEX!

In Germany, Karl Heinrich Ulrichs, a lawyer and journalist, and a homosexual himself, is already campaigning for the rights of homosexuals.

In 1864, he dares speak of the "enigma of love between men".

WHY AM I INEXORABLY ATTRACTED TO YOU?

THAT'S SIMPLY THE ENIGMA OF LOVE.

He is certainly the first homosexual to come out in public.

SEXUAL FREEDOM! FREEDOM TO LOVE!

POOF!

WE'RE NOT THERE YET.

The word "homosexuality" is invented in 1869 by the Hungarian psychiatrist, Kertbeny. Before the talk had been of sodomites and inverts.

OR PEDERASTS. NICE, EH?

The act of naming homosexuality profoundly alters the representation of the sexes, and establishes a bourgeois sexual order which opposes a fertile and normal heterosexuality with a pathological and reprehensible homosexuality.

GOOD   BAD

The great German psychiatrist Magnus Hirschfeld will fight all his life for a better understanding of homosexuality and for its decriminalization.

MEIN GOTT! TOO RIGHT...

WE'RE NOT THERE YET!

We are in London, in 1891. Oscar Wilde is the great poet of the moment, known for his extravagance. Lord Alfred Douglas of Queensbury is a young nobleman, a poet himself, and very handsome.

DID YOU KNOW YOUR FATHER WAS A THIEF? HE STOLE ALL THE STARS FROM THE SKY TO PUT THEM IN YOUR EYES.

OH, YOU'RE A POET TOO...

It was love at first sight for both.

Oscar and Douglas travel together from Paris to Florence to Algiers. They tear strips off each other like Verlaine and Rimbaud.

AND YOU DARE TO CALL ME YOUR DORIAN GRAY?! THAT SWINE?!!

BUT... BUT...

They visit brothels and young prostitutes, publically flaunting a homosexuality condemned by all.

HE'S MY MAN, HE IS!

HMM...

NOT IF YOU COMPARE ME TO DORIAN GRAY AGAIN.

The Marquis of Queensbury, Douglas's father and a member of the House of Lords, provokes Wilde by referring to him as a sodomite.

WHAT'S MORE, THAT VILE SODOMITE DARED TELL MY SON I WAS A THIEF!

BUT... BUT...

Accused of homosexuality, Wilde is condemned to two years forced labour for "gross indecency".

When he leaves prison, Wilde wants to convert to Catholicism and retire to a monastery. The Jesuits refuse.

NO SODOMITES HERE!

YOU SURE?

So Wilde seeks refuge in France, with Gide's help. He dies at the age of 46 in penury in Paris, at the hôtel des Beaux-Arts, on 30 November 1900.

Throughout his trial several writers — English and French — make a concerted effort to offer their support. Mention is made of the Greek tradition of pederasty in an attempt to prove that homosexuality is honourable. This is why the French insult "pédé" (for pederast) is still associated with homosexuality even today.

The century draws to a close with great hopes for more recognition of the plight of women — the beginnings of feminism — and for greater understanding of sexual orientation — the beginnings of sexual liberation.

CHAPTER 11

THE 20TH CENTURY: SEXUAL LIBERATION

In the long battle over urges, passions and prohibitions, the 20th century is the point at which the freedom to exist as an individual, independent of family and society, asserts itself for the first time in the West. With feminism, women "become women" and homosexuality is recognized — if not accepted. Technological progress allows for the separation of fertility and sexuality. This is the century in which liberation begins to mean liberty.

Liberation begins in 1889 with Herminie Cadolle's invention of the bra.

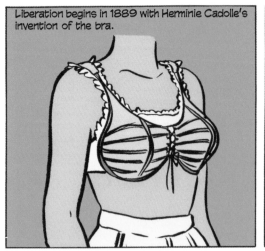

This feminist revolutionary hits on the idea of cutting those very tight corsets in half to free the female body.

BEFORE

AFTER

Modesty is in retreat but religious prohibitions are still very severe: boys and girls are educated separately.

People wash while dressed.

It is a sin to undress. One can only make love in a nightdress in the dark. No private parts should ever be seen.

It is forbidden for men — or even children! — to urinate in public.

MODESTY IN RETREAT

At the end of the 19ᵗʰ century, the woman's body is still smothered and bundled up, covered in layer upon protective layer.

The new fashion for bathing in the sea will free the body, but men and women bathe separately, dressed in trousers or overskirts.

SO SEXY.

OK, MUM? YOU ALL NAKED?

SSSHH!

BEACH HUT

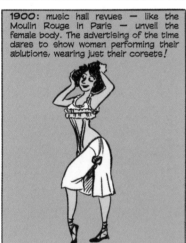

1900: music hall revues — like the Moulin Rouge in Paris — unveil the female body. The advertising of the time dares to show women performing their ablutions, wearing just their corsets!

1906: the great couturier, Paul Poiret, frees the female body, doing away with petticoats and corsets and creating high-waisted dresses.

1920: it's party time — an inevitable response to the massacres of the Great War. The "flapper" is a free and independent woman who is open about her many affairs with men, or even women.

Between the wars, the body shapes of men and women become slimmer, sport and nutrition become important. Plastic surgery arrives. A sense of self emerges with this new consciousness of the body.

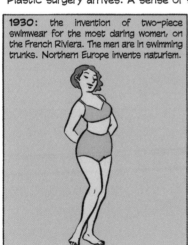

1930: the invention of two-piece swimwear for the most daring women, on the French Riviera. The men are in swimming trunks. Northern Europe invents naturism.

1946: Louis Réaud invents the bikini, named after the Melanesian atoll where an American nuclear bomb has just been tested. A furore among civil and religious authorities who ban them from beaches.

1960: Rudi Gernreich invents the monokini.
1990: the G-string shows off women's buttocks.

The liberation of the female body is one of the major factors in the sexual liberation of the 20ᵗʰ century.

A CHANGING WORLD

The Belle Époque is a time of love, pleasure and adultery for high society and the bourgeoisie, neither of whom are overburdened with moral scruples.

1900: all the great cities are really slumming it — London, Berlin, Brussels... and above all Paris, capital of pleasure.

It's a time of mistresses, demimondaines and scandalous liaisons.

SCANDALOUS LADIES!

Colette and Missy de Morny, overt lesbians, make no secret of their sex parties. Female homosexuality is beginning to come out of the closet. It even becomes "chic" in England and, for a while, far more tolerated. Woohoo!

WOOHOO!

SHOCK! HORROR!

1903: feminism begins to express itself, and powerfully so in the English-speaking world. In Britain the suffragette movement campaigns for women's right to vote. They achieve this in 1918...

GOOD NEWS, WE HAVE THE RIGHT TO VOTE...

YESSS!

BUT ONLY FROM THE AGE OF 30.

OHHH...

... and, ten years later, at the same age as men.

The Abolitionist Federation takes aim at prostitution, a form of female slavery controlled at the time by the police and hidden away in brothels where madams lay down the law. You can recognize these houses by their lanterns and large door numbers.

DOWN WITH SEXUAL SLAVERY!

FREE THE WOMEN!

CLEAR OFF OR I'LL HIRE THE LOT OF YOU!

The prostitutes are supervised in health centres which actually offer them very little protection from STDs. The earliest porn films — still illicit — are made in brothels.

HELLO, DOCTOR. I'M VERY ILL — I NEED YOU TO TAKE GOOD CARE OF ME...

THE DIALOGUE'S FAB...

HOW DID SHE COME UP WITH THAT?

1905: a Viennese physician, Sigmund Freud, shocks the West with his *Three Essays on Sexuality*. He claims that children have a sexuality. Everyone cries wolf: Freud is accused of "pansexualism" — of seeing sex everywhere!

PERVERT!

Freud doesn't back down — he invents the libido and makes pleasure the driving force of sexuality: the libido is an energy, its repression the cause of psychic disorders...

NO! NO! I'M NOT REPRESSING ANYTHING IN THE SLIGHTEST! I'M PERFECTLY HAPPY IN MY CHASTITY, DAMN IT!

...its sublimation, on the other hand, is the source of creativity and works of art.

TO EACH HIS OWN LIBIDO. TO EACH HIS OWN THING.

According to Freud, urges develop in five stages. **The oral stage,** 0-2 years old: the baby sucks on the mother's breast — the model for every loving bond.

The anal stage, 2-3 years old: the baby learns to control its urges.

NOT YET...

NOT YET...

The phallic stage, 3-7 years old: pleasure in showing the genitals.

OOOH! THE LITTLE WINKLE!

The latency period, 7-8 years old: sex seems to be between brackets.

DON'T FORGET TO WASH YOUR WILLY!

MY WHAT?

We know today that this doesn't really exist — that it's an illusion from a time when boys and girls were strictly separated.

The genital stage, in adolescence: sexuality begins to develop into its adult form.

Freud will conclude that the child, capable of seeing any object as a sexual object, is thus a "polymorphous pervert"!

The Oedipus complex is the most famous of Freudian concepts: the unconscious sexual desire for the parent of the opposite sex (incest) and for the elimination of the parental rival (parricide). Hence the little boy, in love with his mother and wanting to kill his father is not a criminal — he is simply suffering from the Oedipal complex.

ON THE OTHER HAND, IF HE WANTS TO KILL BOTH HIS PARENTS IN ORDER TO HAVE SEX WITH THEM, THEN THERE IS CAUSE FOR CONCERN.

But in many respects, Freud is still a man of the 19ᵗʰ century for whom there is only one sex: the male. Those who have it fear its castration.

Those who don't, dream of having one.

OH, IF ONLY I HAD A PENIS...

Female sexuality is still presented as being subject to a male template, the clitoris being an avatar of virility and its enthusiasts regarded as infantile. A "real" woman must spurn her clitoris to enjoy the man's penis instead. This is the source of the great Freudian myth about the existence of vaginal woman and clitoral women.

NOPE, BUT DROP IT — I MUST BE CLITORAL.

Ultimately, for Freud, homosexuality derives from an immature libido arrested in its anal stage.

YOU SEE, MADELEINE, MY LIBIDO IS STILL FAR TOO IMMATURE FOR —

SAY NO MORE, VICTOR — YOU'RE GAY, RIGHT?

ER... IT'S MORE THE FACT I'M 3.

In reality, Freud spoke little of sexuality in his works and did not found a science of sexuality. He said himself that he had never known that sexuality of which some liberated women had spoken, and that he was himself not very comfortable with sexual expression.

IN FACT, DOCTOR FREUD...

YOU WOULDN'T BE A LITTLE BIT ANAL WOULD YOU?

1914-1918: the Great War is not just the carnage we know it have been but also, for those men and women left in its wake, an often desperate love song. The fever of passion defies death and fosters intimacy. Sexual liberation is on the march.

1919: three German doctors — Magnus Hirschfeld, Iwan Bloch and Albert Moll — found the first institute of sexual studies in Berlin. They are the fathers of modern sexology, contributing to the understanding of homosexuality and to the establishment of legal equality between the sexes.

PERVERTS!

The institute in Berlin will be pillaged and its archives burned (an auto-da-fé) by the Nazi authorities in 1933.

A FREE SEXUALITY IS ALWAYS OUTRAGEOUS TO CHURCHES AND TOTALITARIAN REGIMES.

REALLY?

NO KIDDING...

1920: the "kiss on the mouth", still classed in France as a "crime" of "public exposure", becomes a symbol of passionate love over the next few decades...

POLICE!

... after it is popularized by Hollywood.

POLICE!

SSSHHHH!

Even in cultures where people had traditionally brushed noses as a sign of love, as in Japan, people now kiss on the mouth!

In America, Margaret Sanger, a feminist nurse and midwife, founds the Birth Control League (the first case of family planning) and expresses herself freely in her journal, *The Woman Rebel*.

A WOMAN'S BODY IS HERS AND HERS ALONE!

Whereas in France a law officially prohibits abortion and bans all propaganda for contraception.

SHE ASKED HIM TO MAKE A MESS ON THE SHEETS, OFFICER!

The control of men (politicians) over women's intimate lives is still very pronounced...

BUT IT'S CRAZY — YOU DON'T EVEN KNOW WHAT IT IS!

PERHAPS, BUT WE KNOW WHAT'S GOOD FOR YOU.

... while anything that might add to male power is approved: in Paris, the surgeon Serge Voronoff transplants chimpanzee testicles onto impotent men.

QUICKLY, DOCTOR...

HAA! HAA! HA

WELL, OKAY — BUT PUT YOURSELF IN HIS PLACE.

A deluded operation in which many will believe.

OO! OO!

A year later, in Dresden, the first sex-change operation: Rudolph becomes Dora when his penis is replaced with a neovagina.

AVANT   APRÈS

1928: a series of medical discoveries. The gynaecologist Ernst Gräfenberg invents the coil, which he calls the "silver ring", a precious thread coiled in the uterus.

OH! WHAT A PRETTY BRACELET!

AND YOU'LL NEVER GUESS WHERE IT GOES!

He is also the one who, in 1950, will describe the G spot (G for Gräfenberg), a kind of trigger-zone for the female orgasm!

A LITTLE TO THE LEFT... LEFT... RIGHT... LEFT LEFT LEFT   YEEESSSSSSS!

GOT IT!

In 1931, the Japanese gynaecologist Ogino develops, and gives his name to, a method of contraception using temperature charts.

41.7°... ARE YOU SURE WE CAN'T?

Couples free themselves little by little from the constraints of fertility, but the pope still condemns all forms of contraception — even within marriage.

ESPECIALLY WITHIN MARRIAGE!

OTHERWISE, NO MORE BABIES! THINK ABOUT IT!

1936: the psychoanalyst Wilhelm Reich transforms the West with his sexual theories. After *The Function of the Orgasm* in 1927, he preaches sexual revolution.

But his ideas are too far ahead of their time. In contrast to Freud, he thinks that desire must find its expression in the attainment of orgasm. So he invents a machine to capture "orgone", a cosmic energy of nebulous waves.

← orgone-catching machine

For Reich, this cosmic energy fuels the desire for genital contact.

WHAT ARE YOU DOING?

I'M BOOSTING MY LIBIDO WITH COSMIC ENERGY!

1938: Alfred Kinsey, professor of zoology at the University of Indiana, doesn't know how to answer his students' questions on sexuality.

When he turns to his colleagues, he is shocked to discover they don't have a clue either — because no medical research into sexuality exists.

As he has just completed a study of 100 000 bees, Kinsey undertakes the crazy project of collecting the sexual histories of 100 000 human males.

THOUGH THEY WON'T FIT IN THE HIVES...

At the start, his research is beset by obstacles: his work is forbidden and obstructed by the police, the American Medical Association, his university and moral societies. Kinsey does not lose heart, and continues his research.

PERVERT!

PAEDO!

WEIRDO!

SODOMITE!

IT WAS A LOT QUIETER WITH THE BEES.

In the course of this immense study, Kinsey discovers his own homosexuality, which may have been the unconscious spark for his research. He is then seduced by one of his collaborators, who will also become his wife's lover.

I'LL HAVE TO PUT ALL THIS IN MY REPORT.

Kinsey puts the sexual freedom he is now discovering into practice.

1939-1945: the Second World War drives a further evolution in customs which will explode with the Liberation. After five years of occupation, terror and carnage, Europe wakes to the sound of liberated movie sirens, of American crooners, of urges too long repressed. In 1944, in France, women are granted the right to vote, though they will have to wait until the following year before they can do so.

1946: Marthe Richard, whose name is associated with the closure of the brothels, is an adventuress.

TIN TIN NIN TIIIN TIN TIN NIIIN ♪

When still very young, she experiences the "slaughter" of the military brothels where prostitutes turn more than 50 tricks a day.

NEXT!

She becomes ill and catches syphilis; she is put on the National Prostitution Register.

THE BIG BOOK OF "WHORES" BY THE POLICE

In 1916, when she is 26, she meets Louis Richer, who marries her and gets her off the street. Another life opens up for her. An aviation fanatic, she is one of the first women to fly. Under the codename "Alouette" (lark), she serves as a spy in the Great War.

YEEE HAAAA!

A Parisian councillor in 1946, she leads a vote for the closure of the brothels: 1400 are consequently closed in France, and almost 200 in Paris alone. It is a great victory for the abolitionists.

THANK YOU SO MUCH — YOU'VE FREED US.

IT'S TRUE — IT'S FANTASTIC, BUT WHAT'S GOING TO HAPPEN TO US NOW?

And above all the National Prostitution Register — in which she is still named — is destroyed.

HOW ARE WE SUPPOSED TO GO SEE WHORES, NOW?

But clandestine brothels — the "maisons de passe" — pop up. From this point on, prostitutes will drum up business for themselves.

50 FRANCS A TRICK!

50 FRANCS A TRICK!

25 FRANCS A TRICK!

HOTEL

YOU'RE SLASHING THE PRICE!

The exploitation of women (pimping) is prohibited.

BUT IT STILL GOES ON...

1948: forgotten during wartime, Kinsey publishes his report, which wakes up the West. He reveals truths that no one wants to hear.

SOOO...

80% of men have had sexual relations before marriage.

50% of married men have had an affair.

60% of boys remember having experienced homosexual activity during their preadolescence.

etc.

And he reveals the reality of masturbation (which causes no diseases!), sodomy, zoophilia, oro-genital practices such as fellatio, cunnilingus...

APPARENTLY MASTURBATION DOESN'T MAKE YOU DEAF, AFTER ALL.

WHAT?

HEY, YOUR DOG'S CUTE...

Five years later, in 1953, his report on women's sexuality is even more revolutionary: he rehabilitates female pleasure, which is often very precocious (16% of women have erotic experiences before the age of 10).

HEY! SHALL WE PLAY DOCTOR?

OH YESSS!

It confirms the normality of masturbation and of female homosexuality.

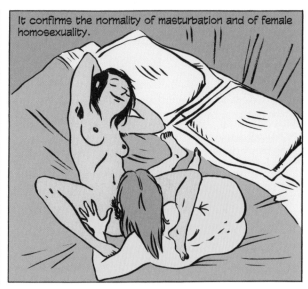

His report is judged to be scandalous. Treated as immoral, Kinsey loses the support of the Rockefeller foundation, putting an end to his research.

COMMUNIST!

BUT... BUT...

1949: a moral liberation is underway. The climate of sexual awakening permeates the public consciousness. Literature, the spearhead of freedom, conveys this modern aspiration. Henry Miller publishes *Sexus*, and Simone de Beauvoir *The Second Sex*.

ER... SIMONE

ONE IS NOT BORN WOMAN, ONE BECOMES WOMAN.

1950: though she becomes a "major" at 21, every young French woman reverts to being a "minor" (under the tutelage of her husband) when she marries.

GREAT!

I CAN'T WAIT TO GET MARRIED!

Most notably she must have his approval before undertaking any professional activity or opening a bank account.

AND SO WHO'S THIS BIG GIRL GETTING A BANK ACCOUNT ALL TO HERSELF?

BANQUE

1952: the fight for the emancipation of women entails freedom from the constraints of pregnancy. Contraceptive methods develop and, in London, the International Family Planning Movement is established.

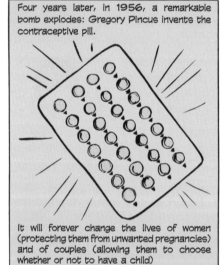

Four years later, in 1956, a remarkable bomb explodes: Gregory Pincus invents the contraceptive pill.

It will forever change the lives of women (protecting them from unwanted pregnancies) and of couples (allowing them to choose whether or not to have a child)

For the first time in the history of humanity, sexuality and fertility are separated, paving the way for the sexual liberation of the 1970s.

NO MORE SERIAL PREGNANCIES!

AT LAST WE CAN SCREW WITHOUT STRESS!

There are some strong reactions: in the United States moral societies try to oppose the pill, and in the Vatican Pope Paul VI forbids its use.

PEOPLE GETTING LAID JUST FOR THE HELL OF IT? WHAT NEXT?

FRUSTRATED OLD GIT!

The authorities delay its approval: 1960 in the United States, 1968 in France. But its use won't be widespread until 1980. With the pill comes the age of pleasure!

THANKS TO THE PILL WE'RE SCREWING LIKE RABBITS!

AND HAVING A WHALE OF A TIME!

1954: in secret, in the basement of a hospital in Saint-Louis, Missouri, the first (and only) direct observation of human sexuality begins. It follows on directly from the work of Alfred Kinsey.

YESSSSSS!

OOOYESSS!

William Masters is professor of gynaecology; he works with Virginia Johnson, his assistant, observing the sexual responses of men and women.

In order to do so they invent some special gadgets: "Ulysses", a transparent plastic dildo, allows a mini-camera to film the changes in the vagina during arousal...

BUT!... THAT'LL NEVER FIT INSIDE!

IT'LL BE FINE. IT'S NOT LIKE IT'S A MOVIE CAMERA.

NO NEED TO MAKE A FUSS

... and electrodes record muscle tension, heart rate, etc. Masters and Johnson themselves will participate in their experiments, and this will, inevitably, bring them together to become an emblematic couple.

BY THE WAY...

DO YOU FANCY GOING FOR DINNER SOMETIME?

Initially, the subjects — men and women — were prostitutes; then there were volunteers.

I'M COMING IN THE NAME OF SCIENCE.

The results are revolutionary: the woman's sexuality is absolutely distinct from the man's, despite what had previously been thought. The clitoris is the principle source of orgasmic pleasure.

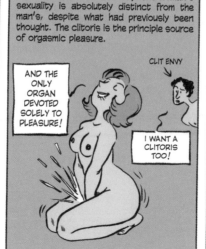

AND THE ONLY ORGAN DEVOTED SOLELY TO PLEASURE!

CLIT ENVY

I WANT A CLITORIS TOO!

There is no point at which sexuality stops, and no age limit for sexual satisfaction.

ER... FANCY MAKING IT FOUR TIMES?

OH, I'M ON FIRE!

THE GREAT CHANGE
1960 — 1970

Over the course of a few decades, the West is transformed from a traditional into a modern society — one of the greatest revolutions since humanity began.

All traditional societies are organised in an identical manner:

At the top, divine powers

Next the ancestors and the elders — the wise men

At the heart of this structure, a family, a clan, a village, a society form **the group**

The destiny of each individual is decided by his or her family, his or her group. Women are further subjugated still.

The couple is not about love, and eroticism is absent.

In this second half of the twentieth century, in modern society, **the individual subject** appears — a great revolution — choosing his or her own path in life independent of the family and the group.

This change is radical.

The large family, at the heart of which the husband and wife struggle for intimacy, is replaced by **a couple** made of two individuals — who desire and love each other — and their children. This is the culmination of the marriage of love...

This new social organization breaks apart the "family interests" which had prevailed since humanity began, and the intimacy of the couple takes on a new dimension — carnal, erotic. Sexual liberation becomes a reality.

In the United States, it's the hippy revolution. The children of the baby-boom create a counter-culture which spurns traditional values, preaching pacifism, a return to nature and sexual freedom.

The hippies live in communes, rejecting marriage and the family. They experiment with free love and with everything that consenting adults can experience together.

FINGERS CROSSED THIS NEVER ENDS.

The hippy movement is like a laboratory for this new age of sexual freedom.

This is also the time of the first Gay Pride (1969), an annual event to proclaim the rights of homosexuals.

GAY LIBERA DAY

SING IF YOU ARE GLAD TO BE GAY

GAY LOVE IS GOOD LOVE ♥

Hi MOM GUESS WHA

In France, this great transformation explodes into a revolutionary youth movement in May 1968: a campaign for a new society, for greater freedom, and for sexual liberation.

HERE'S YOUR BALLOT PAPER:

Communal experiments — in hindsight utopian ones — aim to deconstruct the family, and society.

HE'S SO CUTE!

WHO'S THE FATHER?

YOU THREE!

Wilhelm Reich's ideas for a sexual revolution now become very influential. Young homosexuals demand their freedom. Michel Foucault denounces the social control of sexuality.

PLEASE TELL ME...

THIS DOESN'T APPLY TO HOMOSEXUALS?

P.C.F.

Sex without limits

MY BODY IS **MINE!** WLM

IT BEARS REPEATING FROM TIME TO TIME.

In 1969, the French Women's Liberation Movement (WLM) demands "the end of male oppression", and "free and available abortion for all".

Contraception is approved in late 1968 and abortion decriminalized (the Veil law) in 1975.

From now on sexuality can be the free expression of desire.

SEX SYMBOLS

The 20th century is marked by the advent of love in the cinema, and the cult surrounding the male and female stars of these love stories.

Of the men, it's Rudolph Valentino who drives the women of the 1930s wild. Later it will be Clark Gable, Marlon Brando or James Dean, according to the tastes of each era. For sexual attraction too is subject to fashion.

In the 1930s and 1940s, the actress Mae West becomes a movie idol. A liberated woman in her own life as she is on the screen, she uses high heels to make herself taller and a tight corset to emphasize her bust. Her swaying walk makes her famous.

IS THAT A GUN IN YOUR POCKET, OR ARE YOU JUST GLAD TO SEE ME?

This is the image that American aviators have in mind when they name their inflatable life jackets "Mae Wests" — the name they still go by today.

Next Rita Hayworth, Sophia Loren, Marilyn Monroe and Brigitte Bardot will take on the role of the perfectly proportioned "femme fatale": long legs, narrow waist, generous bust — the embodiment of sex appeal.

In the 1960s, a young and delicate silhouette emerges under the gaze of David Hamilton — flat chest, skinny, with long legs...

... incarnated in the 1970s by the almost androgynous model Twiggy.

STICK-THIN, BASICALLY.

Then, in the 1980s, a more natural and sporty physique, in the image of Jane Fonda, invades our screens.

ALWAYS NATURAL — WHATEVER THE POSE.

1970-1980

The evolution in sexual customs is dramatic. In a single decade, centuries of prohibitions fall away: sexual experiences and living together before marriage become common; the shackles of premarital virginity are broken; most births now occur outside marriage.

In June 1974, *Emmanuelle*, a film by Just Jaeckin, comes out which tells the story of a young, liberated woman and her lover, Mario, who is 40 years older.

Its release is both a scandal and a triumph. This much-maligned film will be seen by almost 9 million filmgoers in France and 45 million worldwide — one of the most successful French films of all time. It coincides with the liberation of morals and the abolition of film censorship.

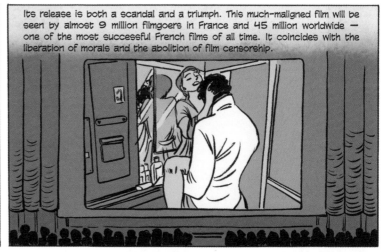

The next year, a French law restricts the release of X-rated films — those that are overtly sexual and pornographic. Porn is ghettoized in dedicated cinemas.

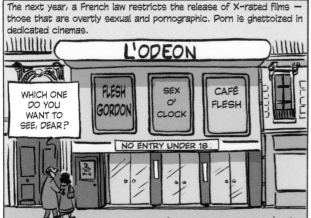

WHICH ONE DO YOU WANT TO SEE, DEAR?

L'ODEON

FLESH GORDON

SEX O' CLOCK

CAFÉ FLESH

NO ENTRY UNDER 18

1980: in France, the Minitel — a kind of precursor to the Internet — inspires a new kind of sexual encounter.

TOO HOT!

3615 ULLA

1981: it is striking that the AIDS epidemic arrives at the very moment that syphilis, rampant for the last 500 years, is finally eradicated. Thousands of men and women — with homosexuals the first to suffer — die of Acquired Immune Deficiency Syndrome. There have been around 40 million deaths since the start of the epidemic.

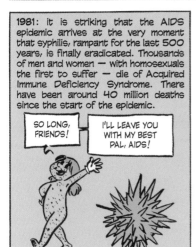

SO LONG, FRIENDS!

I'LL LEAVE YOU WITH MY BEST PAL, AIDS!

A reaction swiftly follows: "safe sex" — a combination of protection (condoms) and a reduction in the number of sexual partners.

HOW MANY PARTNERS DID YOU HAVE BEFORE ME?

NOT A CLUE — I DIDN'T COUNT THEM.

PUT TWO CONDOMS ON THEN.

1982: France decriminalizes homosexuality which is now only a misdemeanour. However, it will still be classified as a mental illness by the WHO until 1991!

DAD — I'M CURED!

REALLY? YOU'RE NO LONGER A LESBIAN?

YES, BUT IT'S NO LONGER AN ILLNESS.

NEW SEXUAL ORDER

In France a new society progressively establishes itself in which no real moral judgements are made about sex.

Anything goes between two consenting adults.

There is only one prohibition: the intrusion of adult sexuality into the world of children.

The denunciation of moral crimes, still common at the start of the century, disappears. Adultery, no longer a criminal offence in France since 1975, remains a civil offence — though one that is no longer prosecuted from the 1990s onwards.

Sexual freedom blossoms among couples, and a kind of libertinage emerges in the form of "wife swapping" — where couples are free to exchange partners, often in specialist clubs (a practice that remains very marginal, however).

The century draws to a close with the invention of Viagra (1998), the first effective therapy for male impotence, and thereafter widely used for recreational sex...

... and in 1999 the introduction of the PACS (civil pact of solidarity) in France allows for civil partnerships, including between same-sex couples — a precursor to "marriage for all".

174

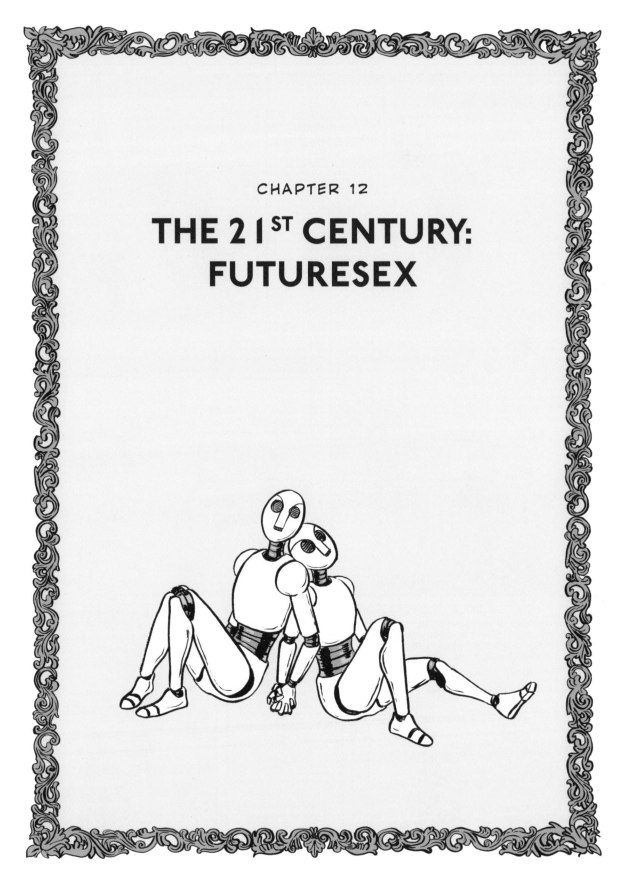

The first two decades of the 21ˢᵗ century are already rich in their evolution in relation to sex, its depiction, and its practices... The future will be even richer.

2000 - 2010: the real start of the internet as a popular phenomenon, a global network which profoundly changes human relationships.

YOU COULD WRITE TO ME FROM TIME TO TIME!

HOW AM I SUPPOSED TO DO THAT? YOU HAVEN'T GOT AN EMAIL ADDRESS!

For the last few decades, social evolution has been considerable: a steady decline in married couples, the impact of divorce, a reduction in the duration of couples' relationships, a rise in the number of stepfamilies...

Social networks magnify these trends.

ER... SWEETHEART? YOUR STATUS ON FACEBOOK IS "SINGLE" — IS THAT NORMAL?

EITHER WAY, YOU'VE GOT LOTS OF NEW FRIEND REQUESTS.

Pornographic websites are legion (almost 200 000 freely accessible sites in France alone). One in two adolescents has seen a porn film by the age of 11. Sexual addiction to images is becoming a reality.

WHAT? YOU MEAN THERE'S BETTER STUFF OUT THERE THAN M & S CATALOGUES?

YOU BETCHA! THOSE LINGERIE PAGES ARE FOR BABIES!

Equality between men and women has made real progress, but differences remain (the average female salary is still only three quarters of its male equivalent).

I HAVE TO SAY THAT IN TERMS OF PRODUCTIVITY THERE'S NO COMPARISON!

OH, YOU'RE RIGHT THERE!

Gender studies, pioneered in the 1990s by Judith Butler, applies itself to the social arena — notably to avoid the reinforcement of gender stereotypes among children: pink for girls, blue for boys... Sexual identities are thus constructed from the images of sexuality offered by society.

I WANT TO PLAY WITH HIS LORRY!

I WANT TO WEAR PINK!

NO!

YOU MIGHT TURN GAY!

Every sexual orientation is now possible: homosexuality, heterosexuality, bisexuality, transsexuality, gay couples, straight couples... But each orientation needs to be put into perspective. In a recent French poll: 2.2 % of men and 1.3% of women declared themselves to be gay or bisexual (survey of sexuality in France, 2008).

A reality, however, which the Catholic church refuses to face — as it only stands up for the family made of a daddy, a mummy and their children.

THE SAME HAPPY AND MODERN FAMILY FOR EVERYONE!

2001: beginning in the United States, online dating sites proliferate and specialize (match.com, EHarmony.com., Meetic.com). Amorous encounters are no longer left to chance...

COME ON! HANDSOME, INTELLIGENT, CULTURED, GOOD SENSE OF HUMOUR — HE SOUNDS PERFECT! WHY DON'T YOU GO FOR A DATE WITH HIM?

THAT'S MY BROTHER.

Some sites are overtly devoted to sex and to particular erotic practices (wife swappers, adulterers, cougars, fetishists, BDSM...) People meet according to sexual orientation (straight, gay, lesbian, bi), religious faith, ethnicity, or identity...

WE MET ON A SITE FOR TRANSSEXUALS, KOREANS, CATHOLICS, REDHEADS, AND MOUSTACHE FETISHISTS. HOW ABOUT YOU?

ON MATCH. COM.

The internet allows for the social and public recognition of sexual minorities — some of whom are still suppressed. Each year Gay Pride takes on greater importance, demanding rights for gay, bi, and trans people.

The European Parliament demands that all member states of the Union grant equal rights to same-sex couples.

2004: the first gay marriage is celebrated in France. Stéphane and Bertrand are married by Noël Mamère, the mayor of Bègles.

AS THE SEX OF SPOUSES IS NOT SPECIFIED IN THE CIVIL CODE...

... I NOW PRONOUNCE YOU MAN AND HUSBAND!

There are violent reactions: insults, threats...

DOWN WITH THE GROOMS!

The marriage will be annulled three years later. Homophobic attitudes resurface. The fight for gay/straight equality is not over.

NO! IT'S "HUSBAND AND WIFE" NOT "MAN AND HUSBAND"! THAT'S JUST HOW IT IS!

ANNULLED!

2002: Nathalie Rykiel popularizes sex toys.

They are displayed in shop-windows in Paris, in the heart of Saint-Germain-des-Prés. The French, now uninhibited, discover mechanized auto-eroticism!

BEFORE

SEX SHOP

CUT PRICE!

BLOW-UP DOLLS

DVD X RAYON GAY

SEX SHOP

HOT

AFTER

SEXY SHOPY ♡

2010: Roxxxy, the first interactive sexual robot, is presented at the Adult Entertainment Expo in Las Vegas. Her soft skin is synthetic, her intelligence artificial, her sex — female!

SHE'S PERFECT...

BUT SHE LOOKS LIKE SHE'S JUST DIED.

Roxxxy is available with a choice of five personalities: reserved, extrovert, dominant, young or experienced! A long-term companion for an attentive man.

I'M GOING TO LEAVE ROXXXY.

I CAN'T TAKE IT ANYMORE. SHE'S TOO COLD. SHE'S EITHER SHY OR EXTROVERT — BUT THERE'S NOTHING IN BETWEEN.

UH-HUH... AND HOW ABOUT TRYING TO LIVE WITH A REAL WOMAN?

JUST SAYIN'...

As for Sybian, he's existed for over 20 years — a male sex machine able to dish out 100 orgasms in a row.

YES YES YES YES YES YES YES YES YES YES YES YES YES YES YES YES YES YES YES YES

In Japan, the Kiss Transmission Device has just been invented, a device to exchange kisses via the internet.

And for many years, electric sex toys have allowed shrinking violets to find satisfaction alone.

YOU CAN'T STOP PROGRESS!

2013: the adoption in France of the "marriage for all" (or Taubira) law, which makes marriage for same-sex couples possible.

GRANNY, ERIC AND I ARE GOING TO GET MARRIED!

ARE YOU GAY?

Many are against the law — celebrities, politicians, and above all the Catholic church — and also against surrogate motherhood. The "DEMO FOR ALL" in Paris brings 300 000 to 1 million demonstrators together.

NO TO THE TAUBIRA LAW!

WE CAME AS A FAMILY TO SHOW THAT EVEN CHILDREN ARE AGAINST GAY MARRIAGE!

YEAH! ...

WHAT'S GAY MARRIAGE?

ONE DAD ONE MUM

A significant segment of French society seems not to understand what sexual orientation is, doubtless because of a lack of sex education.

A MAN IS MADE TO BE WITH A WOMAN. END OF.

THEY COULD HAVE JUST CHOSEN NOT TO BE GAY, AND THEN THEY COULD HAVE GOT MARRIED LIKE EVERYONE ELSE.

GAYS HAVE AN UNBRIDLED SEXUALITY THAT COULD CORRUPT CHILDREN.

THEY MIGHT TRY TO ADOPT CHILDREN IN ORDER TO SODOMIZE THEM!

2014: the LGBT community defends the rights of lesbians, gays, bs and trans, but also asexuals and queers. The battle for the recognition of "sexual minorities" is not over either.

OH, NO — WE'RE NOT HOMOPHOBIC! WE JUST DON'T WANT YOU TO HAVE THE SAME RIGHTS AS US!

YOU BET — WE'RE NOT MEAN OR ANYTHING!

I SEE — YOU'RE ACTUALLY NICE "HATERS"...

2015: the internet connects nearly three billion surfers with over a billion websites online. Social networks speed up communication which is now globalized.

HAVE YOU SEEN MY BOYFRIEND? HE LIVES IN AUSTRALIA.

COOL! HAVE YOU MET HIM YET?

NO, BUT IT'S SERIOUS — WE'RE GOING OUT TOGETHER ON FACEBOOK, TWITTER AND WHATSAPP!

Location-based encounters (Grindr, Tinder, happn) do away with the rituals of seduction by offering immediate encounters with potential sexual partners nearby – and this is not some new kind of prostitution.

WHOSE DICK IS THIS?

COME OUT, COME OUT, WHEREVER YOU ARE! GRINDR SAYS YOU'RE LESS THAN TWO METRES AWAY!

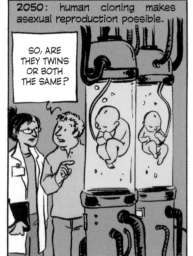

Love substitutes are developed: cerebral implants for those suffering from paralysis. Orgasmic brain stimulation is now possible.

2060: worldwide decriminalization of homosexuality.

AIDS is now under control, but Z-Prim now emerges, the first STRV (Sexually Transmitted Resistant Virus).

SYPHILIS, AIDS, Z-PRIM... WHAT NEXT?

WE'LL NEVER BE ABLE TO SCREW IN PEACE!

Global emergency measures: all oral or genital contact is now forbidden.

FORTUNATELY, THERE'S ALWAYS CONDOMS.

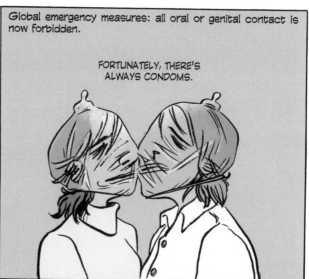

2080: the world population reaches 10 billion, despite the halt to reproduction in the G20 countries, as average life expectancy settles at around 130 years. The fight against the Z-Prim epidemic is starting to succeed, but sexual identities have evolved in the meantime and a sexuality freed from the constraints of human relationships has rapidly developed.

Auto-eroticism is free and artificial, using implants, devices and holograms...

Addictions to VFS (Very Free Sex) increase. People spurn an antiquated sexuality that was too conventional in responding purely to sexual reflexes.

WHAT IS THAT?

2200: Orbipolis, the great international megalopolis of East Africa, located in the very cradle of humanity (a powerful symbol of a return to our origins), is the seat of the World Parliament, gathering together the nations of the Great Alliance formed in the wake of the rising waters.

We are now in a technological society which has definitively separated sexuality and reproduction...

At its head are enhanced humans with totally virtual sexualities (orgasms on command thanks to chips implanted in the brain).

Androids oversee the reproduction of the human race in factories conceived for this purpose: genes are rigorously selected, and birth-rates tied to death-rates to avoid population growth.

The human biomass lives in an urban and ultradigital world. Men and women are sterilized at birth and genetically modified. Sexual appetites no longer exist. Augmented reality glasses allow everyone to move around without bumping into each other, all while living parallel lives in a digital universe.

But on this day...

SAW M-482
NOAH D-142
SUBJECTS IDENTIFIED. THERE IS A BUG IN THE PROGRAM. AN UNCONTROLLED GENETIC MUTATION.

SEND SOME DRONES TO SEARCH WITHIN A 50 KILOMETRE RADIUS OF ORBIPOLIS.

A little later, in the forest of Niambe, two kilometres from Orbipolis...

WE HAVE A SIGNAL. THEY'RE IN NIAMBE.

BUT...

WHAT ARE THEY DOING?

183

MEMO

This memo is a short synthesis
of the fundamental ideas explored
in *The Story of Sex*. It aims to answer
questions often left unresolved.

LOVE

While there are some presages of love in the animal kingdom (courtship rituals, offerings, attachments...), the feeling of love seems to be characteristic of human relationships. In traditional societies, the ritual known as "seduction" among humans is a male privilege. This patient courtship — over several months, or even several years — ritualized in dances, invitations, secret trysts... is often cut short in modern societies when it would often be worth reviving: this is one of the secrets to enduring relationships.

Is love a choice? Not really. First and foremost it's the emotions that do all the talking and choosing for lovers. However, traditionally, the family and society have long imposed their will. Today, when individuals are free to make their own decisions, attraction is sparked by a first glance, a glimpse of a silhouette, or a face... The voice is one of the most personal of the signals we send: timbre, inflections, a particular accent are all instruments of seduction. **The kiss** thus plays a very special role. It is the most intimate contact one can have, for touch, sound, taste and smell all combine to foreshadow sexual intercourse. The kiss often conveys more emotion than a lengthy declaration. It's the union of physical and emotional love, an unbreakable bond that brings human beings together.

Emotion at its most intense, love at first sight paralyses, transports, devastates. It's Racine's Phaedra seeing Hippolytus for the first time: "I saw him, I blushed, I turned pale before him" (*Phaedra*, I.3). This kind of love is a psychological encounter. Then, through the magic of hormones, the bond crystallizes: the brain in love awakens. Oxytocin, dopamine and endorphins bring us to the verge of ecstasy.

Then comes the great metamorphosis which leads from passionate to **lasting love**, and creates a relationship that can stand the test of time. For time is evidently the great obstacle that love must overcome! How can one make the excitement of those first days last? How can one keep the passion alive? Does love really only last three years? Obviously not — it lasts as long as the authenticity of our feelings.

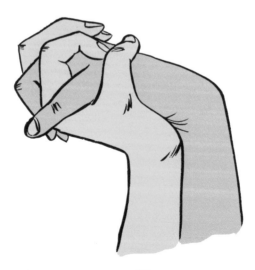

EDUCATION

We know today that human sexuality is not innate: it is learned and constructed through the images that society offers us. Even among our cousins, the primates, who live in a natural habitat, sexuality is learned through experience — young monkeys witness the courting and frolicking of the adults. The need for a model is evident: a young chimpanzee, isolated from its peers, is paradoxically incapable of mating when it reaches adulthood.

Yet there is a **fundamental difference**. The phenomenon of modesty: humans always make love away from the group. This is one of the great problems with sexuality: on the one hand it requires education; on the other, culture and religion suppress any model and often any form of sexual education.

The first attempts to teach about sexuality date from the 1950s in Europe. Opposition was widespread and aggressive, on the part of the Church as well as among teachers: "Education is a matter for the family." Sex education classes were subsequently written into law but, in reality, rarely delivered.

Sex education is today well established in Northern Europe (the Netherlands, Denmark, Sweden...). Elsewhere, the influence of Church and family often limits this practice. In France, the law of 4 July 2001 stipulates three classes of sex education per year in primary and secondary school. However, as teachers have no training in this very particular field, it is often associations such as those devoted to family planning that ensure these classes go ahead. In most cases, they rarely take place at all and, when they do, they are limited to the three P's: "prevention, pill, protection", in other words information on fertility and STDs. A genuine sex education should take the bio-psychological, emotional and social aspects of sexuality into account, should allow children to understand differences between the sexes, interpersonal relationships, the importance of developing critical thinking, an open mind and respect for the other. In the Netherlands, where a complete programme of sex education is delivered from primary school upwards, the rates of unwanted pregnancies and abortions is the lowest in the world.

Porn: in the absence of any real sex education, young adolescents will seek information from their peers and from the only iconographic model of sexuality — porn. This is quite evidently the worst possible model, and the reason why a more reliable source of knowledge is indispensable, from primary school right through to the last year of secondary. By the age of 11, one in two adolescents has already watched porn.

PROHIBITIONS

From the beginning, all societies have decreed prohibitions concerning sexuality. These vary greatly according to culture, religion and period. In the course of the long history revealed in this book, we have seen, for example, the prohibition then the acceptance of homosexuality, masturbation, and free sexual behaviour...

The incest taboo is the first of these. It's the renunciation of sexual desire towards the members of one's own clan, a foundational law for humanity. In the animal kingdom there is already an avoidance of incest through the exogamy of young females (see pp. 20-21) who leave their community at puberty to go and live in another group away from their biological father. Females also distance themselves from their young male offspring as soon as they become too frisky. The human taboo is far more fragile, conveyed by language, stories and myths. It is transgressed too often. But there are no reliable statistics regarding incest, a matter too private ever to be openly admitted. An inquiry by the International Association of Victims of Incest in 2009 estimates that it affects 3% of the general population. This is doubtless a low estimate.

Religious prohibitions come next: the duty of celibacy or chastity; the ban on sex before marriage; the ban on adultery; the ban on divorce; the repression of auto-eroticism (masturbation); the ban on sodomy; the ban on contraception... There are also **legal and societal prohibitions**: penalties for sex with children (incest and paedophilia); penalties for non-consensual sex; penalties for rape in marriage... It is by respecting these fundamental prohibitions that sexuality can now be freely lived, without moral judgement, between two consenting adults and according to a very simple rule: do nothing that might make someone else feel uncomfortable.

MARRIAGE

Whether one lives in a monogamous or polygamous society, marriage traditionally performs the same function. For the sake of procreation, it unites a man and a woman (and today in some countries, two men or two women). It is only very recently (the 19th century in Europe) that this union has taken on a sentimental dimension (the marriage of love).

Monogamy/polygamy: if one looks at human cultures in their entirety, one sees that monogamy is in the minority, and polygamy in the majority. Societies which claim to be monogamous have laws forbidding remarriage without divorce. In polygamous societies there can be second and third marriages concurrently... with one unspoken caveat: remarriage is only possible for men! Polygamy is a sign of male domination.

Globalization: under the cultural influence of Western societies, Christian marriage (consensual, monogamous and indissoluble) tends to impose its model on the whole world, and the preference for a single union begins to prevail even in countries where polygamy is enshrined in law.

There are still sadly far too many early and forced marriages, imposed by families, mainly in sub-Saharan Africa (where over a quarter of girls aged between 15 and 19 are married), South-East Asia and South America.

In the laboratory of the West, the union of two individuals is in complete flux, with a drop in those getting married (in France 55% of births happen outside marriage), the possibility of same-sex marriage, and of a series of "slices of life" — relationships with different partners in the course of a lifetime. Two adult individuals can thus "become a couple" according to the conditions they choose.

This great freedom which Western societies offer is not without its problems. The lack of a rigid framework and of religious, familial or social prohibitions means that young couples must find their own way, if they are not to go their separate ways.

This is the price of living and loving freely.

POLYGAMOUS BISEXUAL MARRIAGE

NORMALITY

Within this world of great freedom, we tend to say that there is no such thing as a "normal" sexuality — for every relationship is different, whether it is with oneself, with one or more partners, frequent or occasional, with a partner of the same sex or a different one. One rule is worth remembering, however: everything is possible when it comes to sexual relations between two adults only as long as there is consent and no coercion.

History: as *The Story of Sex* has shown, history is a series of instructions and condemnations when it comes to sexuality. Each culture, each religion, each era defines its own normality, and does so for its own ends — for example, reproductive sex is the only kind allowed by Christianity.

Personal life: "what is normal?" is, however, the question most frequently asked by adolescents discovering their sexuality. "Am I normal?" "What about the shape of my breasts?" "The size of my penis?" And now that sex is everywhere: "Am I a good lover?"
These legitimate questions should not become causes of anxiety. Sex education, and the support of teachers, doctors or psychologists should allow adolescents to express their concerns and to grow in confidence.

Some myths: the size of a boy's penis is a red herring. Except in very rare cases, such a boy is really talking about the size of his self-esteem! Vaginal or clitoral? Another myth, for women have many routes to pleasure — tenderness, touch, orgasm... Whether they are vaginal or clitoral — all orgasms are created equal!

Porn addiction: this happens when internet images become the sole source of sexual arousal and education. This can never be a substitute for real encounters. Here once again self-confidence and learning about how to relate to others offer answers to the sense of isolation that emanates from screens.
The average age of first sexual encounter among European countries: 15.6 (Iceland), 15.9 (Germany), 16.1 (Denmark, Sweden), 16.5 (Austria, Norway), 16.6 (the Netherlands, UK), 17.2 (France, Belgium), 17.5 (Spain, Greece), 18.1 (Italy).

ORIENTATION

Orientation designates an individual's sexual attraction to a particular gender: if someone is attracted to a member of the same sex, this is described as homosexuality; if it is to a member of the opposite sex, heterosexuality; if is to members of both sexes, bisexuality. Taking the reproduction of the species as an imperative, the great religions have always privileged only fertile union (between a man and a woman) and condemned infertile (homosexual) attraction. The long history we have traced amply demonstrates the tradition of prosecuting homosexuality until recent times in the West: in France, the last of these victims, Bruno Lenoir and Jean Diot, were publically burnt alive in Paris, at the Place de Grève, on 6 July 1750! Today, homosexuality is still subject to a death penalty in six countries (Saudi Arabia, Iran, Nigeria, Mauritania, Sudan and Yemen) and to corporal punishment, prison, or judicial proceedings in over a hundred countries.

In Western countries where it is easier to reveal one's sexual orientation, the proportion of homosexuality and bisexuality is 3-4% for men and 1-2% for women. But the social acceptance of homosexuality is still often a problem, as the demonstrations against "marriage for all" in France clearly showed.

Identity/Orientation: it is important to clarify the distinction between identity and orientation, for this issue creates considerable confusion. Sexual orientation is not a matter of identity — whatever one's orientation (gay, straight, bi) the individual lives as a man or as a woman. By contrast, transsexualism describes a conflicted sexual identity: individuals have a profound sense of not belonging to the sex they were assigned at their birth. They therefore seek to transform their bodies to align with how they feel. This can be very painful. These bio-psychological cases are rare (1 out of 100 000 to 400 000 people).

PERVERSION

"Perversion" is an old word with moralistic connotations to describe an individual "turning from the straight and narrow". It is associated with ideas of possession and manipulation. Because of this moralistic context, we now use the term "paraphilia" to describe an obsessive sexual fantasy that causes the individual distress.

Paraphilias are numerous: exhibitionism (sexual pleasure from displaying one's genitals in public); voyeurism (pleasure from observing others who are naked or having sex); fetishism (pleasure from particular objects or parts of the body); sexual masochism (pleasure from one's own pain); sexual sadism (pleasure from inflicting pain on others); transvestism (dressing in clothes usually worn by the opposite sex), zoophilia (sexual attraction to animals) and all sorts of other practices... These are peculiar, and often unhealthy, ways of experiencing sexual pleasure. In so far as they are practised among adults and without pressure or coercion, they are not illegal. In our free and open society, we don't make moral judgements about what goes on behind closed doors between consenting adults. There is only one great prohibition: the intrusion of adult sexuality into the world of children or adolescents, which is known as paedophilia. Such cases must always be reported and prosecuted.

Perverted personality: we still refer to a "perverted personality" to describe the hold or control an individual may forcibly exert over another individual. Such forms of control are illegal. Those who commit sexual aggression must be reported and its victims given support.

PROSTITUTION

"The oldest profession in the world" no doubt emerged after the establishment of prohibitions that limited access to sex. In marked contrast with so-called "primitive" societies, where erotic play takes place from childhood and where there is little sexual frustration, in the more complex, male-dominated societies characteristic of the human species, the appropriation of females by certain dominant males creates an imbalance. Sex then becomes a commodity to be exchanged against food, presents, money... And in the dominant polygamous structure of traditional societies there will inevitably be those who are "sexually disinherited".

In the course of this long history of human sexuality, we have seen prostitution emerge and grow, first within religions and then within institutions (the municipal brothels in Athens), and ultimately fuelled by poverty, war, migration and despair...

Globalization: prostitution has now become globalized. Male or female, adult or child, it is always a matter of enslavement and often sustained by sexual tourism. It is estimated that 40 million people worldwide prostitute themselves, with 9 out of 10 of these dependent on a pimp. It has also been established that the majority of prostitutes have experienced sexual violence in childhood (between 75 and 90% of male and female prostitutes have suffered sexual abuse, in most cases within the family).

In so-called "developed" countries where sexual frustrations are comparatively insignificant, where eroticism is a part of marital sexuality, prostitution has become marginalized. Many countries (in Europe, Russia, Canada, Australia, South America...) have decriminalized prostitution while still prosecuting pimping. In other countries (United States, China...) it remains illegal at the cost of a high incidence of clandestine procurement.

Abolitionism or regulation? Two questions and two perspectives remain at odds: is prostitution a form of human exploitation which must be abolished? Or is it an activity like any other which should simply be regulated?